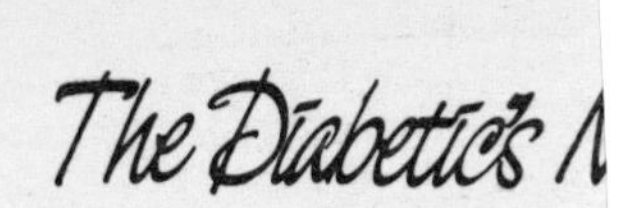

A collection of delicious, nu[illegible] pes that can
be cooked in minutes in the microwave.

By the same author
DIABETIC COOKING FOR ONE
PACKED LUNCHES AND SNACKS

The Diabetic's Microwave Cookbook

Quick and Convenient Meals for the Busy Diabetic

Sue Hall

THORSONS PUBLISHING GROUP

BRITISH DIABETIC ASSOCIATION
London

First published 1986
This new revised edition
first published 1988

Illustrated by Ian Jones

*Photography and styling by Paul Turner
and Sue Pressley, Stonecastle Graphics Limited,
Maidstone.*

The British Library Cataloguing in Publication Data

Hall, Sue
The diabetic's microwave cookbook,
1. Diabetes — Diet therapy — Recipes
2. Microwave cookery
I. Title
641.5'6314 RC662

ISBN 0-7225-1319-4

*Published by Thorsons Publishers Limited,
Wellingborough, Northamptonshire, NN8 2RQ, England.*

Printed in Great Britain by Richard Clay Limited,
Bungay, Suffolk

1 3 5 7 9 10 8 6 4 2

Acknowledgements

The BDA would like to thank Belling & Co. Ltd. and Phillips for their microwave ovens, W. H. Marriage & Sons for their continued help, Corning for their glassware and the many other companies who help us regularly.

I would like to thank Claire Taylor and Christine Speed for help with recipes, and Joy Payne for typing and retyping!

Contents

Recipes

Throughout the book I have used this standard conversion chart:

Weights

25g — 1 oz
50g — 2 oz
75g — 3 oz
100g — 4 oz
150g — 5 oz
175g — 6 oz
200g — 7 oz
225g — 8 oz
250g — 9 oz
275g — 10 oz
300g — 11 oz
350g — 12 oz
375g — 13 oz
400g — 14 oz
425g — 15 oz
450g — 16 oz

Liquid Measures

150ml — ¼ pint
275ml — ½ pint
425ml — ¾ pint
550ml — 1 pint

Spoon Measures

1 teaspoon — 5ml
1 tablespoon — 15ml

It is best to use this to get accurate results.

Introduction

A healthy diet is an important part of diabetic life and should be easy to prepare and eat! Microwaves are becoming very popular in the preparation of quick meals.

Life with a teenage diabetic and work with lots of children at camp soon taught me the importance of 'quick' but healthy meals and snacks. Rather than always reaching for tins and packets of 'fast' food, a microwave can help us to cook food quickly and well which will fit into your carbohydrate or calorie allowance and follow our basic aims of a high-fibre, low-fat, low-sugar diet. Our microwave at the BDA has been a real help with my recipe development and I know lots of families with diabetics use their microwaves.

The aim of this book then is to provide a wide range of high-fibre, reduced-fat, low-sugar recipes to use in our microwave for everyday eating or entertaining.

To obtain good control of diabetes it is important to eat regularly and in the correct quantities. Most people have prescribed carbohydrate and/or calorie allowances and it is important to stick to these. Diet is an important part of good balance.

Remember we are aiming for a high-fibre, low-fat, low-sugar diet within your dietary allowances so all of your food choices are important.

A simple way of guiding your food choices is to use the traffic light system. This will help all of you – even those with no carbohydrate or calorie allowance to select suitable foods. This traffic light system is used in the BDA book *Countdown* (see the suggested reading list on page 90).

Think of your diet instructions as a set of traffic lights directing your diet:
GREEN *for foods you should use;*
AMBER *for foods you can use with caution;*
RED *for foods which shouldn't be used regularly but may be used on special occasions.*

RED – STOP
Don't use these foods except on special occasions.

AMBER – CAUTION
Use these foods with care and not as the largest part of the diet.

GREEN – GO
Use these foods regularly.

Why Do We Stress High-Fibre?

A high-fibre intake is widely publicized as being important to diabetic diet – helping to stabilize blood sugar levels – preventing low or high sugars – and generally improving control. Most people following a high-fibre diet find their control improves generally and they experience fewer hypos – it is good general policy for all of us to eat lots of fibre of course.

These recipes then will help to improve your carbohydrate choices.

What About Fat?

A fairly low total fat intake is part of a good eating plan for all of us because it is now generally accepted that most of us would benefit from eating less fat and in having vegetable rather than animal fats. These recipes will help you to lower your total fat intake.

About the Recipes

As always, the recipes show the total carbohydrate and calorie content and a suggestion of number of portions, with a freezing note to help planning. All the recipes are thoroughly tested. All spoon measures are level and you should only use the *Imperial* or the *Metric* measurements – not mix the two (the recipes have been calculated on the Imperial measurements).

Important Ingredients

A few notes about products you may not have used before.

Flour

(a) Wholemeal and Wholemeal Self-Raising. These are 100% wholemeal flour – containing lots of fibre – you will see I've used them in bread, cakes, puddings and sauces. The self-raising version should always be used if it is specified in a recipe.

(b) 81% Plain and Self-Raising. The figure 81% refers to the extraction rates of the flour during milling, i.e. the amount of the grain left in the flour. These, therefore, contain less fibre than wholemeal but more than white flour. They are still a good compromise choice and often produce lighter results than wholemeal. If my recipe specifies 81% then this should be used to obtain a good result and keep the carbohydrate and calorie figures right.

All of these flours are made by several companies and are available in Health Food Stores and many supermarkets.

Low Fat Spread/Margarine

Always use the fat I have specified – again change will affect calories and the finished product. If you are using low-fat spread choose one of vegetable origin. These are widely available in many supermarkets. Choose soft margarine, not hard.

Fructose (Fruit Sugar)

This is a bulk sweetener sold under the brand names of *Dietade* or *Fructofin* in chemists and supermarkets. In these recipes I have followed normal BDA policy of not counting the carbohydrate so long as one does not have more than 1oz (25g) per day. If you use lots of our recipes in one way or eat fructose or sorbitol in other things you will need to bear in mind the amount of fructose you are eating. The calories in fructose are always counted.

I had great fun creating the recipes and trying them all, I hope you enjoy using them!

1. Healthy Microwaving

What is Microwaving?

A whole new kind of cookery? Yes. You will have to adapt recipes and cooking skills to use your microwave but this and other books will help and practice makes perfect!

Microwave cookery uses electromagnetic waves to create heat within the food and cooks from the outside in – just like ordinary cooking so the standing time is very important to allow cooking to finish. Food may look a little different from your microwave but will taste just as good – if not better!

Remember to read the instructions for your oven very carefully and have fun with lots of recipes.

Practical, Healthy Microwaving

There is no reason why, used carefully, a microwave oven should not be a very healthy way of cooking. There are however several basic points about microwaving which are important.

1. Always read the instructions for your own machine very carefully. Machines differ so you may have to experiment slightly with cooking times and temperatures. (These recipes were tested in a Phillips Microwave 700 watts).

2. Always undercook rather than overcook. Standing time is *very* important and you should always follow the recipes. Food cooks slightly during the standing time.

3. You will see that many of our recipes tell you to cover food with

cling film – this helps to retain the moisture and flavour. Piercing the top is essential to allow some steam to escape.

4. Never use metal in your microwave. It interferes with the microwaves and stops the food getting hot. Specially designed plastic, glass and china are best.

5. Always pierce food which has a skin or membrane.

6. Never try to fry in your microwave – it's dangerous – not to mention adds lots of fat!

Healthy Cooking
There are also ways of making your recipes healthier:

1. Always trim fat off meat and poultry. Skin poultry and fish. Try to allow time to let your mince for pies etc. go cold so you can skim off the fat and then reheat it to use in the finished dish.

2. Use the absolute minimum added fat to cook with.

3. Use herbs instead of salt where you can.

4. Always use skimmed milk in cooking.

5. Choose wholegrain pasta, brown rice or jacket potatoes to accompany your meals. As you will see all of these cook well in the microwave.

6. Use wholemeal or 81% flour in sauces, gravy etc., as well as for baking.

7. Use your microwave to help with healthy recipes – to cook staple foods quickly (rice, pasta and potatoes) and to replace soaking when using dried fruit.

Dried Fruits in the Microwave

Often recipes call for dried fruits to be soaked overnight to rehydrate them and to bring out their sweetness. Using your microwave will mean that you don't have to soak them overnight.

Apricots or Peaches or Pears or Apple Rings

Place 5oz (150g) of fruit in a 2 pint (1 litre) bowl and pour on 1 pint (550ml) of boiling water. Microwave on HIGH for 4 minutes. Allow to stand for 20 minutes.

Prunes

Place 5oz (150g) of fruit in a 2 pint (1 litre) bowl and pour on 1 pint (550ml) boiling water. Microwave on HIGH for 6 minutes. Leave to stand for 20 minutes.

Note: The standing time is just as important as the cooking time.

Preserving in Your Microwave

One of the most noticeable advantages of making preserves in the microwave is the ease and cleanliness of the whole operation. There are no sticky heavy saucepans and no over-cooked jam to scrub away. As well as this, time is reduced and jars can be sterilized in the time it takes to boil water. However, the maximum amounts of jam made in the oven at any one times does not exceed 2lbs (900g) of fruit, so unless your oven handbook states otherwise it would be advisable to keep within this quantity.

The times given in the recipes are those that produced successful preserves in the BDA test kitchen. If you find that the jam or marmalade is done before the stated time is up, or needs more cooking, then do as you think best. The times will not only vary from fruit to fruit but to the ripeness of each fruit and the model of your microwave. To be sure that setting time has been reached check that the preserve has reduced in volume and deepened in colour. Then carry out one of the following tests:

a) **Flake test** – dip a wooden spoon into the preserve and then hold it above the bowl horizontally until it has slightly cooled. Then turn the spoon on its side and if the preserve drops run together and break off cleanly then the preserve is at setting point.

b) **Cooled plate test** – put barely a teaspoon of preserve onto a plate that has been in the refrigerator for a while and allow it to cool. If the surface of the preserve is set and crinkles when you push it with your finger then the preserve is at setting point.

As you will see in the recipes in Chapter 6 less water is needed than in the conventional recipes. This is because in conventional methods a lot of the water is lost from boiling vigorously for a longer time. The quantity of fructose (fruit sugar) in our recipes is half or less than half of the quantities of sugar you will find in ordinary recipes because fructose is about twice as sweet.

Where the recipes tell you to stir the preserve it is important to do so as stirring foods helps to distribute the heat more quickly to the centre of the bowl and will avoid over-cooking and excessive stickiness at the edges. The preserves will splash during heating so it would be a good idea to cover the bowl with cling film in the initial stages of jam making and wiping out your oven with a damp soapy cloth immediately afterwards.

Finally, before embarking on your microwave ventures please note that foods high in fructose/fruit sugar absorb microwave energy very quickly and they also reach very high temperatures so be careful when handling large bowls of bubbling preserves to and from your oven.

2. *Soups and Starters*

Lots of healthy beginnings for your meals

Carrot and Orange Soup

Serves 6 Total CHO – 30g Total Cals – 115

1 medium onion, chopped
8oz (225g) carrots, peeled and sliced
¾ pint/425ml water
Sea salt and freshly ground black pepper
1 large orange

1. Place onion, carrot, water and seasoning in a large glass bowl. Cover with cling film – pierce the top.
2. Microwave on HIGH for 6-8 minutes. Add grated orange rind.
3. Liquidize the soup. Add orange juice. Replace cling film.
4. Microwave on HIGH for 2 minutes. Serve.

Each portion is 5g CHO and 20 calories.

Note: This recipe freezes well.

Spicy Red Soup

Serves 5 Total CHO – 45g Total Cals – 240

1×15oz (425g) can of tomatoes
1 medium onion, chopped
1×8oz (225g) can of red kidney beans
½ pint (275ml) water
½ teaspoon cumin
Pinch of garlic salt
Sea salt and freshly ground black pepper

1. Place all the ingredients in a large bowl. Cover with cling film and pierce the top.
2. Microwave on HIGH for 10 minutes.
3. Stir well. Blend or liquidize.

Each portion is 10g CHO and 50 calories.

Note: This recipe freezes well.

Winter Vegetable Soup

Serves 5 Total CHO – 55g Total Cals – 280

2oz (50g) lentils, washed
1¼ pints (700ml) water
1 small onion, chopped
2 carrots, peeled and chopped
1 medium potato, washed and chopped not *peeled*

1. Place the lentils in ½ pint (275ml) water, cover with cling film and pierce the top.
2. Microwave on HIGH for 6 minutes.
3. Add vegetables and remaining water. Replace cling film.
4. Microwave on HIGH for 6 minutes.
5. Stir, re-cover and microwave for a further 6 minutes.
6. Blend or liquidize and season as required.

Each portion is 10g CHO and 55 calories.

Note: This recipe freezes well.

Cream of Mushroom Soup

Serves 4 Total CHO – 40g Total Cals – 450

2oz (50g) low-fat spread
8oz (225g) mushrooms, chopped
1 small onion, chopped
2 tablespoons wholemeal flour
½ pint (275ml) skimmed milk
1 pint (550ml) chicken stock

1. Place the low-fat spread in a 4 pint bowl. Melt on HIGH for 1 minute.
2. Add the mushrooms and onion and stir. Cover with cling film and pierce the top. Microwave on HIGH for 4 minutes.
3. Add the flour and stir.
4. Gradually add milk and stock, stirring all the time. Replace cling film.
5. Microwave on HIGH for 2 minutes. Whisk and serve.

Each portion is 10g CHO and 115 calories.

Note: This recipe freezes well.

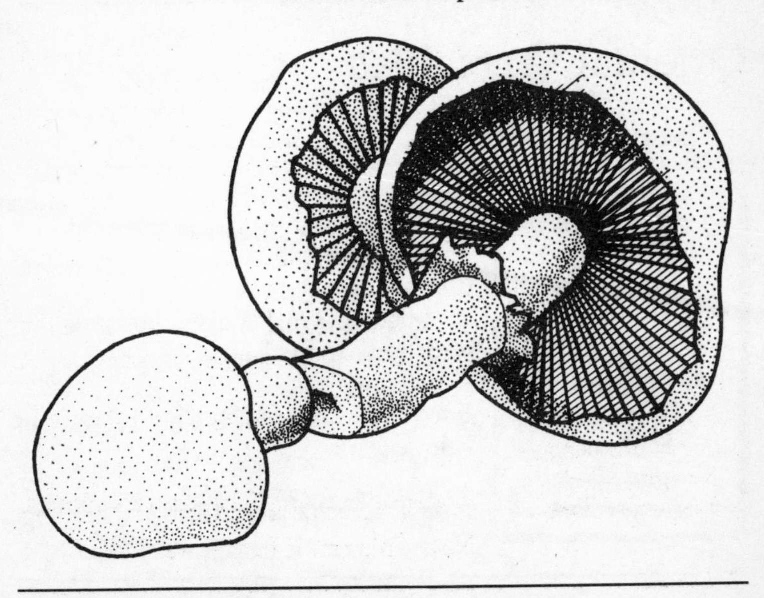

Onion Soup

Serves 4 Total CHO – 40g Total Cals – 380

2oz (50g) low-fat spread
1lb (450g) thinly sliced onions
5 teaspoons wholemeal flour
1½ pints (725ml) beef stock

1. Place the low-fat spread in a 4 pint bowl. Melt on HIGH for 1 minute.
2. Add the onions and stir.
3. Cover with cling film and pierce the top. Microwave on HIGH for 5 minutes.
4. Add the flour and stir. Gradually add the stock stirring well.
5. Replace cling film. Microwave on HIGH for 5 minutes.
6. Stir well and serve.

Each portion is 10g CHO and 95 calories.

Note: This recipe freezes well.

Oriental Vegetables

Serves 4 Total CHO – 15g Total Cals – 120

1lb (450g) mushrooms
8oz (225g) beansprouts
2 onions, finely chopped
1 stick of celery, sliced
Ground ginger
Soya sauce
½ pint (275ml) chicken stock

1. Place vegetables, ginger and soy sauce in a large bowl with stock. Cover with cling film – pierce the top.
2. Microwave on HIGH for 3 minutes. Stir well. Serve immediately.

Each portion is less than 5g CHO and 30 calories.

Note: This recipe is *not* suitable for freezing.

Hummus

Serves 5 Total CHO – 25g Total Cals – 300

½ onion, chopped
1 tablespoon vegetable oil
4oz (100g) canned chick peas, drained
Lemon juice
2 tablespoons natural low-fat yogurt

1. Place onion and oil in a bowl. Cover with cling film and pierce the top. Microwave on HIGH for 2 minutes. Add chick peas and stir.
2. Replace cling film. Microwave on HIGH for 2 minutes.
3. Add remaining ingredients. Liquidize and chill.

Each portion is 5g CHO and 60 calories.

Note: This recipe is *not* suitable for freezing.

Chicken and Corn Pots

Serves 4 Total CHO – 40g Total Cals – 410

4oz (100g) potato, diced
1 carrot, diced
1 stick of celery, chopped
¾ pint (425ml) stock
¼ pint (150ml) skimmed milk
3oz (75g) sweetcorn
6oz (175g) chicken, cooked and chopped

1. Place potato, carrot, celery, stock and milk in a large bowl. Cover with cling film – pierce the top.
2. Microwave on HIGH for 10 minutes or until vegetables are tender. Stand for 5 minutes.

Each portion is 10g CHO and 100 calories.

Note: This recipe is *not* suitable for freezing.

Hot Fruit Kebabs

Serves 5 Total CHO – 50g Total Cals – 200

1 banana, peeled and sliced
1 red apple, sliced
2 pineapple rings (canned in natural juice) drained and chopped
1 large orange, peeled and divided into segments
Lemon juice
Cinnamon

1. Place alternate pieces of prepared fruit on *wooden* skewers, dividing the fruit evenly between 5 skewers.
2. Mix lemon juice and cinnamon. Brush onto fruit.
3. Place kebabs on a ceramic dish and microwave on HIGH for 2 minutes.
4. Brush again with juice. Microwave for a further 2 minutes.
5. Serve immediately.

Each kebab is 10g CHO and 40 calories.

Note: This recipe is *not* suitable for freezing.

Spicy Hot Grapefruit

Serves 2 Total CHO – 10g Total Cals – 40

1 large grapefruit
1 teaspoon dried ginger
Liquid sweetener to taste

1. Slice grapefruit in half and loosen segments.
2. Sprinkle ginger evenly over halves.
3. Microwave on HIGH for 2 minutes.
4. Sweeten to taste and serve.

Each portion is 5g CHO and 20 calories.

Note: This recipe is *not* suitable for freezing.

3. Main Courses

Interesting ways to prepare main meals

Prawn Creole

Serves 5 Total CHO – 15g Total Cals – 325

1×15oz (425g) can tomatoes
1 medium onion, chopped
1 green pepper, chopped
Sea salt and freshly ground black pepper
1 teaspoon curry powder
8oz (225g) prawns – frozen or fresh

1. Place all the ingredients except the prawns in a large ceramic or glass bowl. Cover with cling film and pierce the top.
2. Microwave on HIGH for 7 minutes. Stir in prawns.
3. Microwave on HIGH for 4-8 minutes or until thoroughly heated through.

Each portion is less than 5g CHO and 65 calories.

Note: This recipe freezes well.

Tuna Bread Flan

Serves 7 Total CHO – 70g Total Cals – 850

4 medium slices of wholemeal bread
1oz (25g) low-fat spread
Water to bind
1×6oz (175g) can tuna in brine, drained
3 size 3 eggs
¼ pint (150ml) skimmed milk
Sea salt and freshly ground black pepper

1. Place bread in a food processor or liquidize until fine breadcrumbs are achieved.
2. Mix in low-fat spread.
3. Add enough water to bring to a soft dough. Press into an 8in (20cm) ceramic or glass flan ring.
4. Microwave on HIGH for 4 minutes, or until dry to the touch.
5. Sprinkle tuna over case.
6. Mix egg and milk together with seasoning in a large ceramic/glass bowl.
7. Microwave on HIGH for 4 minutes – stirring after 2 minutes.
8. Pour onto tuna. Microwave on MEDIUM for 7-10 minutes or until soft, but set, turning twice during cooking.
9. Allow to stand for 10 minutes.

Each portion is 10g CHO and 120 calories.

Note: This recipe is *not* suitable for freezing.

Kedgeree

Serves 4 Total CHO – 180g Total Cals – 1560

1lb (450g) smoked haddock
1 tablespoon lemon juice
1 pint (550ml) boiling water
1oz (25g) low-fat spread
1 medium onion
8oz (225g) long grain brown rice
2 eggs, hard boiled and chopped

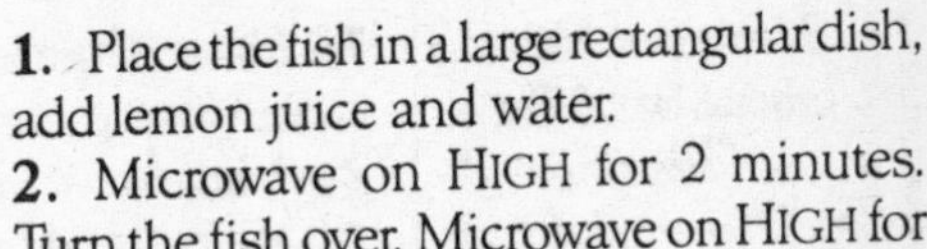

1. Place the fish in a large rectangular dish, add lemon juice and water.
2. Microwave on HIGH for 2 minutes. Turn the fish over. Microwave on HIGH for 2 minutes.
3. Remove the fish, reserving the stock. Flake the fish and keep warm.
4. Place low-fat spread and onion in a 4 pint bowl. Cover with cling film and pierce the top. Microwave on HIGH for 2 minutes.
5. Add the rice and fish stock – replace cling film. Microwave on HIGH for 5 minutes.
6. Stir, re-cover and microwave on HIGH for 5 minutes.
7. Allow to stand for 10 minutes.
8. Stir in fish and egg. Serve.

Each portion is 45g CHO and 390 calories.

Note: This recipe is *not* suitable for freezing.

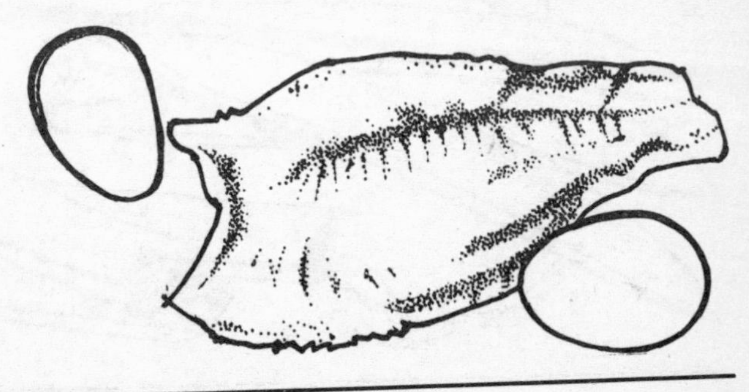

Cod and Green Beans

Serves 2 Total CHO – 25g Total Cals – 470

2 lean cod fillets (about 6oz/175g each)
3oz (75g) fresh/frozen green beans
2oz (50g) sweetcorn
1×10oz (275g) can mushroom soup
1 onion, chopped
Sea salt and freshly ground black pepper
¼ pint (150ml) water

1. Place all the ingredients in a large bowl. Cover with cling film – pierce the top.
2. Microwave on HIGH for 15 minutes. Allow to stand for 10 minutes.

Each portion is about 10g CHO and 235 calories.

Note: This recipe freezes well.

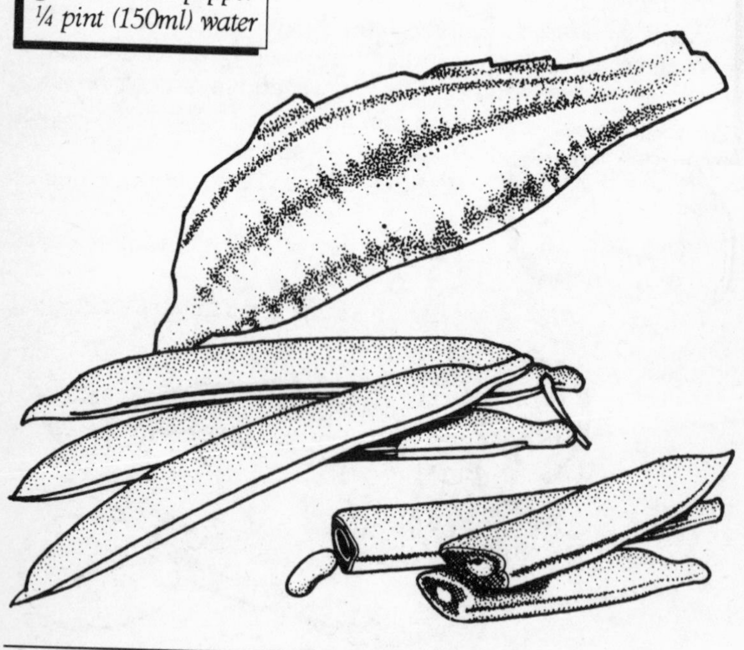

Tuna and Cashew Risotto

Serves 4 Total CHO – 180g Total Cals – 1450

1oz (25g) low-fat spread
1 onion, chopped
1 clove of garlic, crushed
2 sticks celery, chopped
8oz (225g) brown rice
1 pint (550ml) fish stock, boiling
1×6oz (175g) can tuna in brine
1×6oz (175g) can tomatoes
2oz (50g) cashew nuts

1. Melt low-fat spread on HIGH. Add onion, garlic and celery. Cover with cling film and pierce the top. Microwave on HIGH for 2 minutes.

2. Add rice, replace cling film and microwave on HIGH for 1 minute. Stir in stock, re-cover.

3. Microwave on HIGH for 4 minutes. Stir. Microwave for a further 4 minutes.

4. Leave to stand for 10 minutes. Drain off any remaining stock. Add tuna, tomatoes and nuts.

5. Microwave on HIGH for 2 minutes.

Each portion is 45g CHO and 365 calories.

Note: Without the nuts this recipe freezes well.

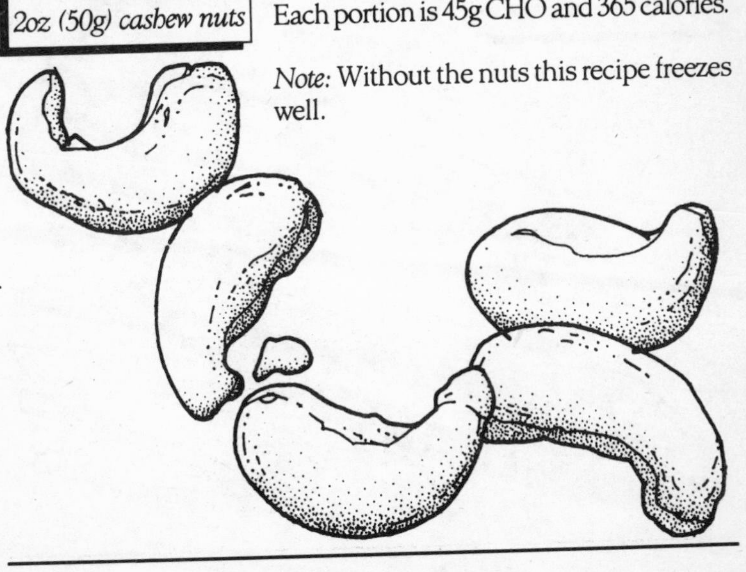

Mackerel Casserole

Serves 3 Total CHO – 30g Total Cals – 600

1oz (25g) celery, chopped
2 medium onions, chopped
1×7oz (200g) can mackerel in brine, drained
1×7oz (200g) can tomatoes
1 small green pepper, deseeded and chopped
4oz (100g) sweetcorn
Sea salt and freshly ground black pepper
¼ pint (150ml) stock

1. Place all ingredients in a large bowl. Cover with cling film – pierce the top.
2. Microwave on HIGH for 15 minutes. Allow to stand for 5 minutes.

Each portion is 10g CHO and 200 calories.

Note: This recipe freezes well.

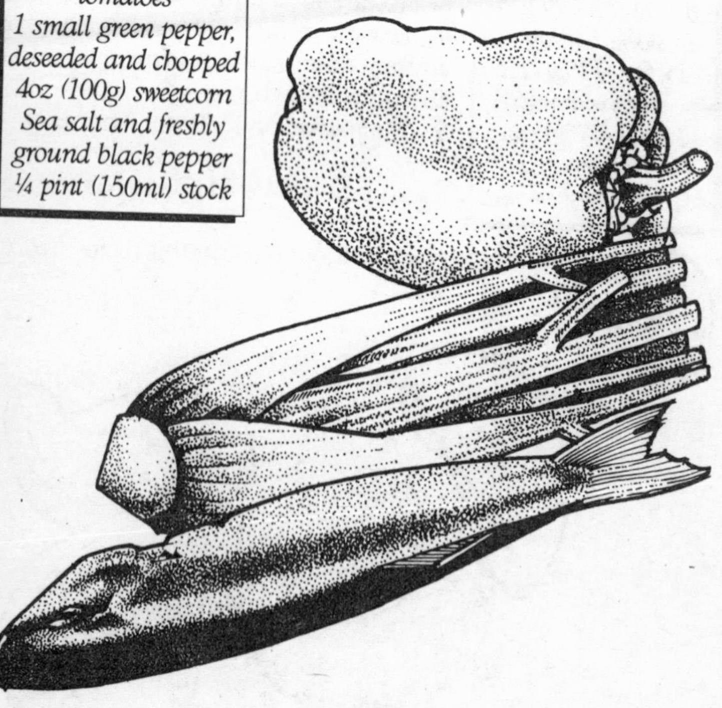

Macaroni Cheese

Serves 5 Total CHO – 150g Total Cals – 1165

2oz (50g) low-fat spread
1oz (25g) wholemeal flour
¾ pint (425ml) skimmed milk
3oz (75g) reduced-fat hard cheese, grated
6oz (175g) wholegrain macaroni, cooked (see page 52)

1. Place low-fat spread in a 3 pint bowl. Microwave on HIGH for one minute.
2. Stir in the flour. Add milk, stirring all the time. Microwave on HIGH for 2 minutes.
3. Whisk, then microwave on HIGH for 2 minutes. Add cheese.
4. Put macaroni in serving dish and pour on sauce. Microwave on HIGH for 2 minutes.

Each portion is 30g CHO and 230 calories.

Note: This recipe is *not* suitable for freezing.

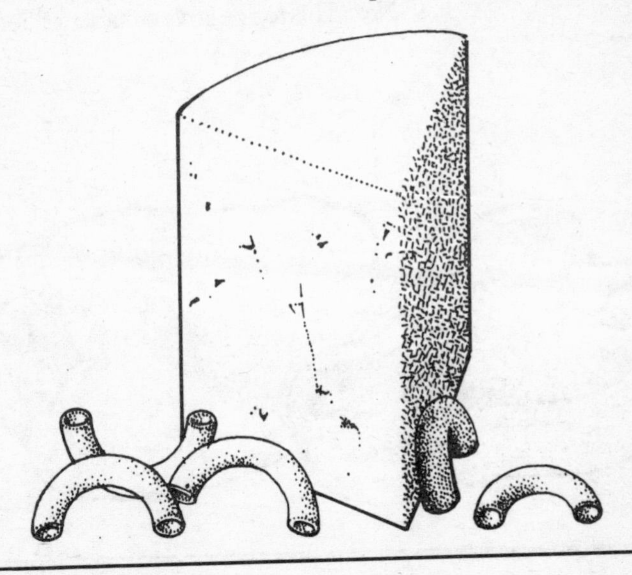

Stuffed Peppers

Serves 4 Total CHO – 120g Total Cals – 665

4 green peppers, deseeded
4oz (100g) cooked brown rice (see page 53)
1oz (25g) aduki beans, soaked and cooked
1oz (25g) fresh wholemeal breadcrumbs
2oz (50g) sweetcorn
1oz (25g) reduced-fat hard cheese, grated

1. Slice pepper in half length ways. Place in a casserole with enough water to cover.
2. Heat on HIGH for 2 minutes. Drain and leave to stand.
3. Mix remaining ingredients except cheese.
4. Fill peppers with rice mixture and sprinkle on cheese.
5. Microwave on HIGH for 3 minutes – until heated through and cheese is melted.

Each portion, i.e. 2 halves of pepper, is 30g CHO and 165 calories.

Note: This recipe is *not* suitable for freezing.

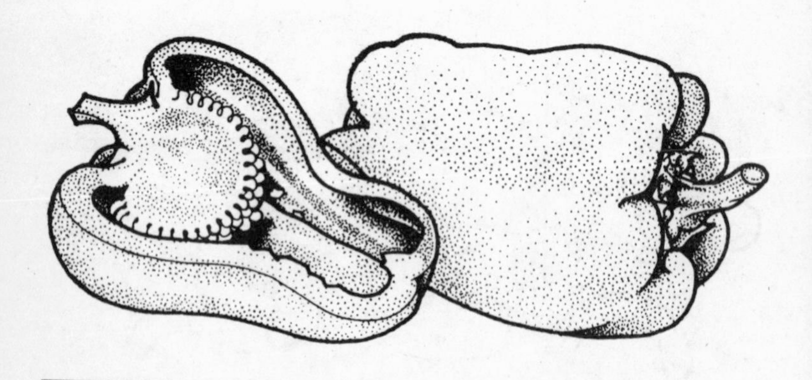

Italian Beans

Serves 4 Total CHO – 120g Total Cals – 710

1 onion, chopped
1oz (25g) low-fat spread
4oz (100g) cooked wholegrain pasta shells (see page 53)
1 green pepper, chopped
1×5oz (150g) can butter beans, drained
1×5oz (150g) can red kidney beans, drained
3 tablespoons stock
Sea salt and freshly ground black pepper

1. Place onion and low-fat spread in a bowl. Cover with cling film and pierce the top. Microwave on HIGH for 3 minutes.
2. Add remaining ingredients and stir well.
3. Replace cling film and microwave on HIGH for 4 minutes, stirring after 2 minutes. Serve.

Each portion is 30g CHO and 180 calories.

Note: This recipe freezes well.

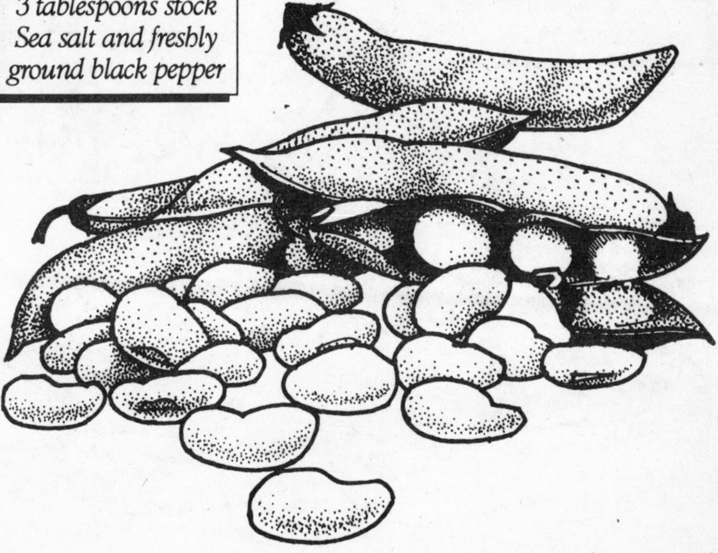

Wholewheat Spaghetti Flan

Serves 6 Total CHO – 125g Total Cals – 900

5oz (150g) wholewheat spaghetti, cooked (see page 52)
1 green pepper, diced
1 onion, chopped
2oz (50g) sweetcorn
2oz (50g) mushrooms, chopped
1×14oz (400g) can tomatoes
2oz (50g) reduced-fat hard cheese, grated
1 egg
½ pint (275ml) skimmed milk

1. Pack spaghetti into a 7in (20cm) deep dish.
2. Top with vegetables and cheese. Beat egg into milk. Pour into flan.
3. Microwave on HIGH for 8 minutes (turning after 4 minutes) or until set.
4. Allow to stand for 10 minutes.

Each portion is 20g CHO and 150 calories.

Note: This recipe is *not* suitable for freezing.

Menu 1: Tuna Bread Flan (page 24) and Spicy Summer Veg (page 57).

Menu 2: Spinach and Cheese Bake (page 56) and Dried Fruit Compote (page 60).

Menu 3: Spicy Red Soup (page 18) and Soda Bread (page 74).

Menu 4: Cheesy Nut Scones (page 73) and oranges.

Oaty Aubergine

Serves 2 Total CHO – 50g Total Cals – 580

2 medium aubergines
1 teaspoon vegetable oil
1 onion, finely chopped
5oz (150g) mushrooms, chopped
Sea salt and freshly ground black pepper
4oz (100g) reduced-fat hard cheese
2oz (50g) oatmeal soaked in boiling water for 20 minutes

1. Top and tail the aubergines. Place on a ceramic plate and microwave on HIGH for 3 minutes. Turn after 2 minutes. Slice into 2 lengthways.
2. Place remaining ingredients (except cheese and oats) in a bowl. Cover with cling film – pierce the top. Microwave on HIGH for 3 minutes.
3. Scoop flesh out of aubergines and mix with vegetables and drained oats.
4. Pile into aubergine cases. Top with grated cheese. Microwave on HIGH for 1 minute.

Each portion, i.e. 2 halves, is 25g CHO and 290 calories.

Note: This recipe is *not* suitable for freezing.

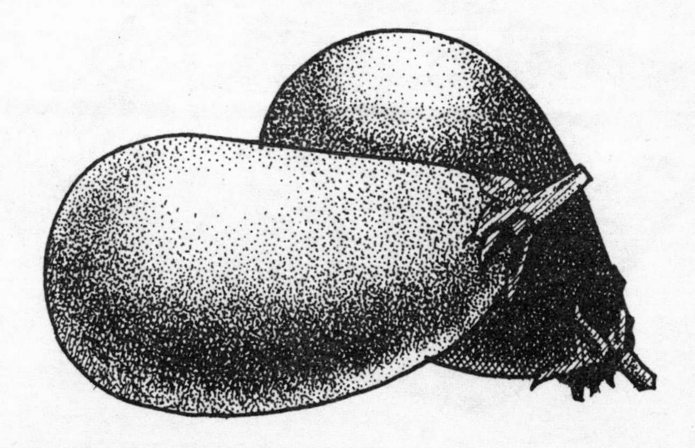

Lentil Lasagne

Serves 4 Total CHO – 180g Total Cals – 1340

6oz (175g) lentils
½ pint (275ml) water
1 small onion, chopped
1 clove of garlic
1 tablespoon vegetable oil
4oz (100g) wholewheat lasagne, cooked (see page 52)
1 egg
½ pint (275ml) White Sauce (see page 55)
1oz (25g) reduced-fat hard cheese

1. Soak lentils in water for 2 hours. Drain. Pour on ½ pint clean water, add onion and garlic and microwave (see page 49).
2. Assemble lasagne using layers of pasta, lentils and white sauce (with egg beaten in) ending with a layer of white sauce. Sprinkle on cheese.
3. Microwave on HIGH for 4 minutes or until cheese is melted and dish is hot through.

Each portion is 45g CHO and 335 calories.

Note: This recipe freezes well.

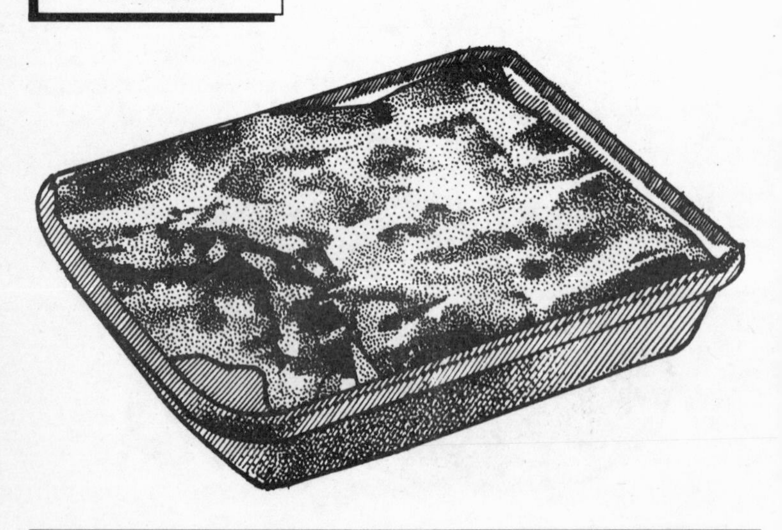

Cauliflower Cheese

Serves 5 Total CHO – 50g Total Cals – 550

1 medium cauliflower, in florets
½ pint (275ml) water
1 pint (550ml) White Sauce (see page 55)
2oz (50g) reduced-fat hard cheese, grated

1. Place cauliflower and water in a large bowl. Cover with cling film and pierce the top.
2. Microwave on HIGH for 8-10 minutes until tender. Leave to stand for 2 minutes.
3. Make up sauce and stir in cheese.
4. Drain cauliflower and pour on sauce.

Each portion is 10g CHO and 110 calories.

Note: This recipe is *not* suitable for freezing.

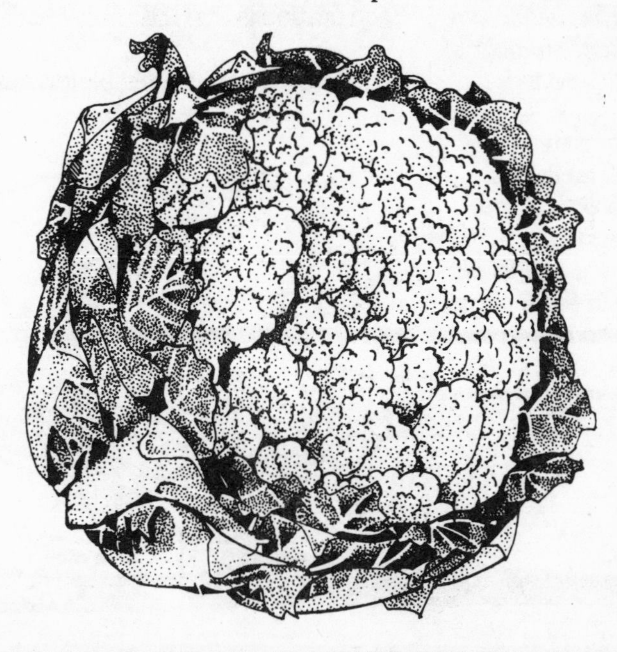

Sweet and Sour Chicken

Serves 5 Total CHO – 70g Total Cals – 465

2oz (50g) frozen green peas
2 tablespoons water
1 small onion, chopped
½ green pepper, chopped
1 large stick of celery, sliced
5oz (150g) chicken, cooked and cubed
1×15oz (425g) can pineapple in natural juice

Sauce
2 teaspoons wholemeal flour
1 chicken stock cube
Sea salt and freshly ground black pepper
1 teaspoon soya sauce
2 teaspoons vinegar

1. Place peas and water in a large bowl. Microwave on HIGH for 2 minutes.
2. Add onion, pepper, celery, chicken and drained pineapple (reserve the juice).
3. In a 2 pint (1 litre) jug mix all sauce ingredients. Add pineapple juice.
4. Microwave sauce ingredients on HIGH for 3 minutes. Stir well.
5. Fold into vegetable mixture. Microwave on HIGH for 4 minutes. Serve.

Each portion is 15g CHO and 95 calories.

Note: This recipe is *not* suitable for freezing.

Chicken and Broccoli Lasagne

Serves 6 Total CHO – 85g Total Cals – 690

4oz (100g) wholegrain lasagne, cooked (see page 52)
4oz (100g) broccoli, chopped
5oz (150g) chicken, skinned and cooked
½ pint (275ml) basic White Sauce (see page 55)

1. Place broccoli in a large bowl with ¼ pint (150ml) boiling water. Cover with cling film and pierce top.
2. Microwave on HIGH for 3 minutes. Drain.
3. Assemble lasagne by mixing chicken and broccoli into sauce and placing alternate layers of sauce mix and pasta in a ceramic or glass dish.
4. Microwave on HIGH for 4 minutes. Serve.

Each portion is 15g CHO and 115 calories.

Note: This recipe freezes well.

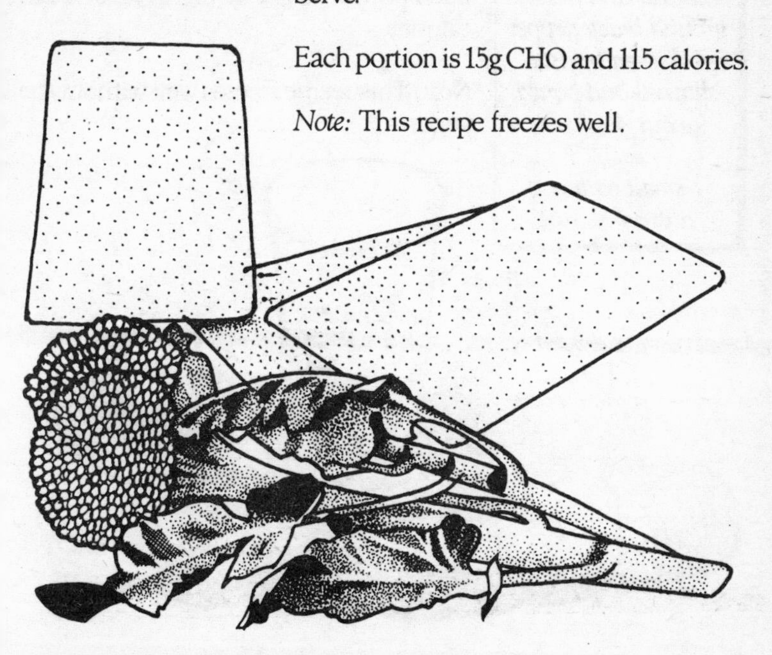

Chicken Chasseur

Serves 4 Total CHO – 50g Total Cals – 850

4 carrots, chopped
1 onion, chopped
8oz (225g) mushrooms, chopped
½ pint (275ml) tomato juice
1 clove of garlic, crushed
½ pint (275ml) stock
3oz (75g) sweetcorn
Sea salt and freshly ground black pepper
4 chicken breasts, skinned and boned (about 4oz/100g each)
1 small carton of natural yogurt

1. Place all the ingredients, except the chicken and yogurt, in a large bowl. Cover with cling film – pierce the top.
2. Microwave on HIGH for 3 minutes. Add chicken and stir well. Replace cling film.
3. Microwave on HIGH for 15 minutes. Allow to stand for 10 minutes.
4. Stir in yogurt just before serving.

Each portion is about 10g CHO and 215 calories.

Note: This recipe freezes well without the yogurt.

Coq au Vin

Serves 4 Total CHO – 10g Total Cals – 700

¼ pint (150ml) chicken stock
¼ pint (150ml) dry white wine
4oz (100g) mushrooms, chopped
1 medium carrot, sliced
1 medium onion, chopped
1 teaspoon oregano
Sea salt and freshly ground black pepper
4 chicken breasts, skinned and boned (about 4oz/100g each)

1. Place all the ingredients, except the chicken, in a large bowl. Cover with cling film – pierce the top.
2. Microwave on HIGH for 3 minutes. Add chicken and stir well. Replace cling film.
3. Microwave on HIGH for 15 minutes. Allow to stand for 10 minutes.

Each portion is negligible CHO and 175 calories.

Note: This recipe freezes well.

Chicken with Ginger

Serves 2 Total CHO – 10g Total Cals – 400

2 chicken breasts, skinned and boned (about 4oz/100g each)
1 teaspoon vegetable oil
8oz (225g) beansprouts
2 medium onions, finely chopped
2oz (50g) root ginger, chopped or 3 teaspoons dried ginger
1 medium green pepper, deseeded and chopped
¼ pint (150ml) chicken stock
1 tablespoon soya sauce

1. Place the chicken breasts on a flat surface and flatten.
2. Heat the oil on HIGH for 1 minute, add the beansprouts, onion, root ginger and the green pepper and microwave on HIGH for 3 minutes.
3. Place in a casserole dish with the stock, soya sauce and the chicken breasts. Cover with cling film – pierce the top. Microwave on HIGH for 15 minutes. Allow to stand for 5 minutes.

Each portion is 5g CHO and 200 calories.

Note: This recipe is *not* suitable for freezing.

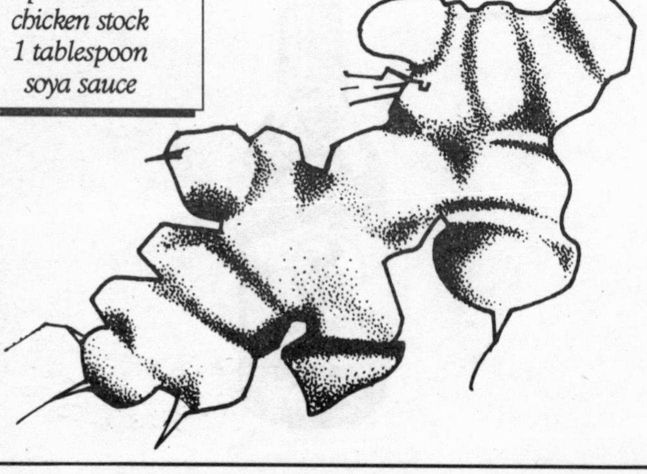

Pineapple Chicken

Serves 2 Total CHO – 30g Total Cals – 380

2 chicken breasts, skinned and boned (about 4oz/100g each)
¼ pint (150ml) pineapple juice
2 rings of pineapple – canned in natural juice, drained and chopped
2 tablespoons dry white wine
½ teaspoon garlic salt
Freshly ground black pepper to taste

1. Place all the ingredients in a casserole dish, cover and leave to marinade overnight.
2. Cover with cling film – pierce the top and microwave on HIGH for 15 minutes.
3. Allow to stand for 10 minutes.

Each portion is 15g CHO and 190 calories.

Note: This recipe freezes well.

Mince with Cheese Topping

Serves 4 Total CHO – 60g Total Cals – 1190

Base

12oz (350g) very lean minced beef
2 medium carrots, grated
6oz (175g) cooked peas
1 large onion, finely chopped
4oz (100g) cooked lentils (see page 49)
¼ pint (150ml) tomato juice
1 medium red pepper, deseeded and chopped
½ teaspoon garlic salt
½ teaspoon thyme
½ teaspoon black pepper

Topping

2oz (50g) reduced-fat hard cheese
1oz (25g) fresh wholemeal breadcrumbs
2 tablespoons Worcestershire sauce
1 medium tomato, chopped

1. Place mince in a large dish. Cover with cling film – pierce the top. Microwave on HIGH for 2 minutes. Drain off fat.
2. Add remaining base ingredients. Replace cling film and microwave on HIGH for 7-10 minutes. Allow to cool and skim off all fat.
3. Recover and microwave on MEDIUM for 3 minutes.
4. Mix topping ingredients together and sprinkle over mince. Microwave on HIGH for 3 minutes. Serve.

Each portion is 15g CHO and 300 calories.

Note: This recipe freezes well.

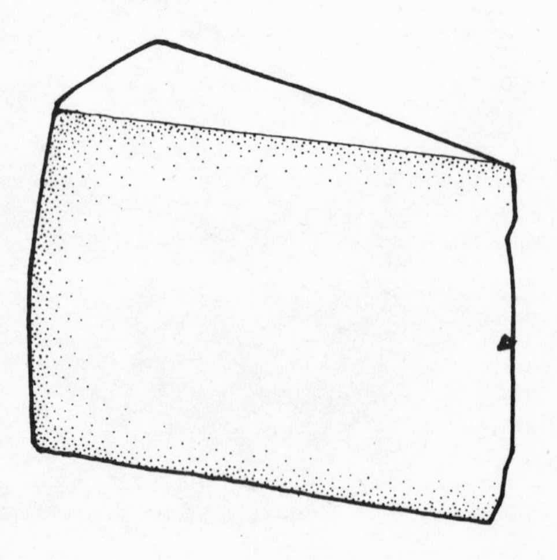

Brown Stew

Serves 5 Total CHO – 30g Total Cals – 620

1 onion, chopped
1oz (25g) low-fat spread
8oz (225g) lean stewing steak, cubed
2 carrots, sliced
1 parsnip, chopped
¼ pint (150ml) beef stock
Sea salt and freshly ground black pepper

1. Place onion, low-fat spread and meat in a bowl. Cover with cling film and pierce the top.
2. Microwave on HIGH for 3 minutes. Stir well.
3. Add remaining ingredients and replace cling film. Microwave on HIGH for 20 minutes. Allow to stand for 10 minutes.

Each portion is about 5g CHO and 125 calories.

Note: This recipe freezes well.

Liver Casserole

Serves 2 Total CHO – 20g Total Cals – 480

1 large cooking apple, cored and sliced
6oz (175g) red cabbage, finely shredded
1 tablespoon wine vinegar
¼ pint (150ml) water
Sea salt and freshly ground black pepper to taste
8oz (225g) lamb's liver, thinly sliced

1. Place the sliced apple and shredded cabbage in a bowl with the vinegar, water, salt and pepper and mix well.
2. Place the sliced liver in a bowl. Cover with cling film – pierce the top. Microwave on HIGH for 3 minutes.
3. Add the apple and cabbage mixture. Replace the cling film and microwave on HIGH for 10 minutes.
4. Allow to stand for 10 minutes.

Each portion is 10g CHO and 240 calories.

Note: This recipe freezes well.

Pork Casserole

Serves 2 Total CHO – 20g Total Cals – 590

8oz (225g) leeks, washed and sliced
2 teaspoons vegetable oil
8oz (225g) shoulder of pork, cubed
2 tablespoons wholemeal flour
½ pint (275ml) brown ale
2oz (50g) mushrooms
1 teaspoon mixed herbs
Sea salt and freshly ground black pepper to taste

1. Microwave leeks in oil on HIGH for 2 minutes.
2. Toss meat in flour, add to leeks, cover with cling film and pierce the top. Microwave on HIGH for 3 minutes.
3. Add remaining ingredients. Replace cling film and microwave on HIGH for 20 minutes.
4. Allow to stand for 10 minutes.

Each portion is 10g CHO and 295 calories.

Note: This recipe freezes well.

Liver and Red Beans

Serves 2 Total CHO – 30g Total Cals – 420

4oz (100g) lamb's liver, sliced finely
1 tablespoon vegetable oil
1 onion
1×5oz (150g) can red kidney beans
1×5oz (150g) can tomatoes
Sea salt and freshly ground black pepper

1. Place the liver, oil and onion in a bowl. Cover with cling film – pierce the top – and microwave on HIGH for 3 minutes.
2. Stir in remaining ingredients, replace cling film and microwave on HIGH for 15 minutes. Allow to stand for 10 minutes.

Each portion is 15g CHO and 210 calories.

Note: This recipe freezes well.

Shepherd's Pie

Serves 4 | Total CHO – 85g | Total Cals – 1000

12oz (350g) very lean mince
1 onion, chopped
½ pint (275ml) stock
Sea salt and freshly ground black pepper
1lb (450g) potatoes, creamed (see page 50)

1. Place mince in a large bowl. Cover with cling film – pierce the top. Microwave on HIGH for 2 minutes. Drain off all the fat.
2. Add onion and stock. Replace cling film. Microwave on HIGH for 7-10 minutes until cooked through.
3. Allow to go cold. Skim off all fat.
4. Microwave the mince on HIGH for 3-5 minutes. Top with potatoes and serve.

Each portion is 20g CHO and 250 calories.

Note: This recipe freezes well.

Quick Pasta Supper

Serves 2 Total CHO – 80g Total Cals – 960

1 clove of garlic, crushed
4 rashers very lean bacon, trimmed and chopped
½ green pepper, chopped
4oz (100g) button mushrooms, sliced
1oz (25g) low-fat spread
1 small carton low-fat natural yogurt
4oz (100g) cooked wholegrain pasta shells
(see page 53)

1. Place all the ingredients – except the yogurt and pasta in a bowl. Microwave on HIGH for 4 minutes.
2. Top pasta with vegetable mixture, pour on yogurt and serve.

Each portion is 40g CHO and 480 calories.

Note: This recipe is *not* suitable for freezing.

4. Vegetables and Accompaniments

Exciting ways to eat lots of veg.

Cooking Lentils

Total CHO – 25g Total Cals – 150

2oz (50g) lentils, washed
½ pint (275ml) water

1. Place lentils and water in a large bowl. Cover with cling film and pierce the top.
2. Microwave on HIGH for 6 minutes. Allow to stand for 5 minutes.

Note: Cooked lentils freeze well.

Potatoes

Jacket potatoes are very quick and easy in the microwave.

Total CHO – 30g Total Cals – 130

To cook a 5oz (150g) potato

1. Wash the potato and prick it with a fork.
2. Place it on kitchen paper.
3. Microwave on HIGH for 2 minutes, turn over and microwave for 3 minutes more.
4. Allow to stand for 2 minutes.

Note: If you cook 2 potatoes you will need to double the cooking times.

Boiled Potatoes

Total CHO – 80g Total Cals – 340

To cook 1lb (450g)

1. Wash and peel the potato in the usual way.
2. Cut into medium equal sized pieces.
3. Place in a casserole with 4 tablespoons of water.
4. Cover with cling film and pierce the top. Microwave on HIGH for 9-11 minutes.
5. Allow to stand for 3 minutes.

These can, of course, then be creamed, etc.

Lyonnaise Potatoes

Total CHO – 85g Total Cals – 450

1oz (25g) low-fat spread
1 medium onion, chopped
1lb (450g) cooked potato, chopped

1. Melt low-fat spread for 1 minute on HIGH.
2. Add onion and stir. Microwave on HIGH for 3 minutes.
3. Add potato and stir well. Microwave on HIGH for 2-3 minutes.
4. Serve immediately.

Note: This recipe freezes well.

Braised Celery

Serves 2 Total CHO – 5g Total Cals – 40

5oz (150g) celery, chopped
1 medium onion, chopped finely
2 tablespoons water

1. Place all ingredients in a bowl. Cover with cling film – pierce the top.
2. Microwave on HIGH for 6-8 minutes until celery is tender.
3. Allow to stand for 3 minutes.

Each portion is about 5g CHO and 20 calories.

Note: This recipe is *not* suitable for freezing.

Carrots

Total CHO – *neg* Total Cals – 35

6oz (175g) carrots, sliced
2 tablespoons water

1. Place carrots and water in a bowl. Cover with cling film and pierce the top.
2. Microwave on HIGH for 6-8 minutes until carrots are tender.

Note: This recipe freezes well.

Cooking Pasta in the Microwave

Pasta cooks well in the microwave. Cooking methods and times depend upon the type of pasta to be used:

Macaroni

1. Place 8oz (225g) wholegrain macaroni in a 2 pint bowl, pour on 1 pint (550ml) boiling water.
2. Cover with cling film – pierce the top. Microwave on HIGH for 3 minutes.
3. Stir, re-cover and then microwave on HIGH for a further 3 minutes.
4. Drain and serve.

Spaghetti

1. Place 8oz (225g) wholegrain spaghetti in a large rectangular dish. Pour on 1 pint (550ml) boiling water.
2. Cover with cling film – pierce the top. Microwave on HIGH for 6 minutes.
3. Allow to stand for 5 minutes.
4. Drain and serve.

Tagliatelle

1. Place 8oz (225g) wholegrain tagliatelle in a 5 pint covered casserole. Pour on 2 pints (1 litre) boiling water. Stir, cover with cling film and pierce the top.
2. Microwave on HIGH for 5 minutes. Allow to stand for 5 minutes.
3. Drain and serve.

Lasagne

1. Place 8oz (225g) wholegrain lasagne in a 2 pint bowl. Pour on 1 pint (550ml) boiling water. Cover with cling film – pierce the top.
2. Microwave on HIGH for 6 minutes. Allow to stand for 5 minutes.
3. Drain and serve.

Pasta Shells

1. Place 8oz (225g) wholegrain pasta shells in a 2 pint bowl. Pour on 1 pint (550ml) boiling water. Cover with cling film – pierce the top.
2. Microwave on HIGH for 3 minutes.
3. Stir, re-cover and microwave on HIGH for a further 3 minutes.
4. Drain and serve.

Microwave Rice

Cooking brown rice in the microwave is easy and successful.

1. Place 8oz (225g) wholegrain rice in a 2 pint bowl. Pour on 1 pint (550ml) boiling water. Cover with cling film – pierce the top.
2. Microwave on HIGH for 4 minutes.
3. Stir, re-cover and microwave on HIGH for a further 4 minutes.
4. Leave to stand until the liquid is absorbed. Serve.

Note: Standing time in these recipes is as important as cooking time.

Sauces

Tomato Sauce

Delicious served with wholegrain pasta.

Makes 1 pint   Total CHO – 30g   Total Cals – 300

2oz (50g) low-fat spread
1 medium onion, sliced finely
1 clove of garlic, crushed
1×14oz (400g) can of tomatoes
1×3oz (75g) can of tomato purée
1 teaspoon dried mixed herbs
Sea salt and freshly ground black pepper

1. Place the low-fat spread, onion and garlic in a large (1 litre) jug and microwave on HIGH for 2 minutes.
2. Add all the other ingredients. Stir well and cover with cling film – pierce the top. Microwave on HIGH for 3 minutes.
3. Stir, re-cover and microwave on HIGH for a further 3 minutes. Serve.

Note: This recipe freezes well.

White Sauce

Makes 1 pint Total CHO – 45g Total Cals – 360

1oz (25g) low-fat spread
1oz (25g) wholemeal flour
1 pint (550ml) skimmed milk

1. Place the low-fat spread in a large (1 litre) jug and melt on HIGH for 1 minute.
2. Carefully stir in flour to a smooth paste. Gradually add milk, stirring well.
3. Microwave on HIGH for 2 minutes. Stir and serve.

Note: This recipe is *not* suitable for freezing.

Cheese Sauce

Total CHO – 45g Total Cals – 485

Simply add 2oz (50g) of grated reduced-fat hard cheese to the basic White Sauce recipe after adding the milk.

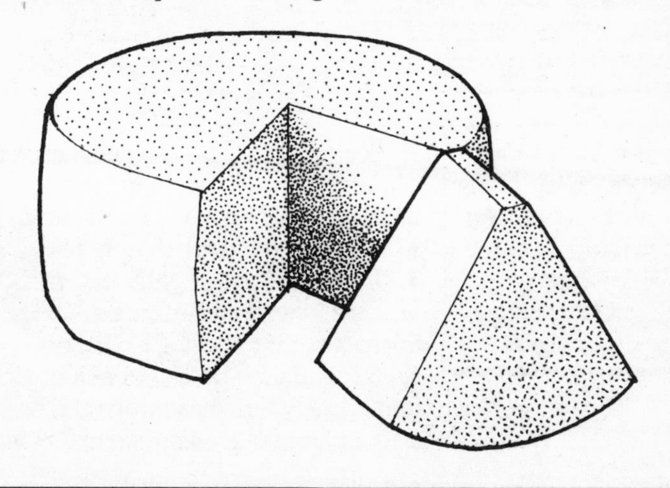

Spinach and Cheese Bake

Serves 5 Total CHO – 25g Total Cals – 520

10oz (275g) spinach, fresh or frozen
1 onion, chopped
3oz (75g) reduced-fat hard cheese, grated
Sea salt and freshly ground black pepper
2×size 3 eggs, beaten
1oz (25g) wholemeal flour

1. Mix spinach and onion in a little water in a large bowl. Cover with cling film – pierce the top. Microwave on HIGH for 4 minutes.
2. Blend in remaining ingredients.
3. Pour into a 9in (23cm) pie dish.
4. Microwave on HIGH for 10 minutes – turning a quarter turn after each 2 minutes.
5. Leave to stand for 5 minutes.

Each portion is 5g CHO and 105 calories. calories.

Note: This recipe is *not* suitable for freezing.

Spiced Beans

Yield 2lbs (1kg) Total CHO – 110g Total Cals – 660

8oz (225g) (dry weight) mixed beans ***— not red kidney***
½ pint (275ml) vinegar
1oz (25g) fructose (fruit sugar)

1. Soak the beans overnight. Drain. Place in a large bowl and cover with boiling water.
2. Microwave on HIGH for 15 minutes.
3. Leave to stand for 15 minutes.
4. Drain and pack tightly into jars.
5. Place vinegar and fructose in a bowl and microwave on HIGH for 2 minutes.
6. Stir and then pour over beans. Cover immediately with plastic tops and store in a cool place for a *maximum* of 2 *months.*

Note: This recipe is *not* suitable for freezing.

Spicy Summer Veg

Serves 3 Total CHO – 15g Total Cals – 75

1 small onion, chopped
2 courgettes, sliced
1 green pepper, sliced
1 small aubergine, sliced, salted, left for 1 hour and then rinsed
2 medium tomatoes, sliced
1 clove of garlic, crushed
Mixed dried herbs
3 tablespoons water

1. Place all the ingredients in a large bowl.
2. Cover with cling film and pierce the top.
3. Microwave on HIGH for 4 minutes. Stir.
4. Replace cling film and microwave on HIGH for 2 minutes.
5. Serve immediately.

Each portion is 5g CHO and 30 calories.

Note: This recipe freezes well.

Winter Veg Casserole

Serves 6 Total CHO – 35g Total Cals – 150

1 onion, chopped
2 medium carrots, sliced
2 parsnips, peeled and sliced
2 sticks celery, sliced
½ pint (275ml) stock
2oz (50g) sweetcorn

1. Place all the vegetables, except the sweetcorn, in a large bowl with stock. Cover with cling film and pierce the top.
2. Microwave on HIGH for 8-10 minutes until vegetables are just tender.
3. Allow to stand for 5 minutes. Stir in sweetcorn. Replace cling film.
4. Microwave on HIGH for 3 minutes.

Each portion is 5g CHO and 30 calories.

Note: This recipe is *not* suitable for freezing.

5. *Desserts and Baking*

New ways to make puddings and cakes

Lime Soufflé

Serves 5 Total CHO – 25g Total Cals – 225

7 fl oz (200ml) low-calorie fizzy lemon and lime drink
2 tablespoons cornflour
1 tablespoon lime juice
Grated rind of 1 lime
1 tablespoon fructose (fruit juice)
Few drops of green food colouring
1 egg yolk
3 egg whites

1. Blend all the ingredients except eggs.
2. Microwave on HIGH for 3-6 minutes, stirring occasionally.
3. Add yolk.
4. Whisk egg whites until stiff and fold in.
5. Turn into a soufflé dish and microwave on LOW for 8 minutes.
6. Serve immediately.

Each portion is 5g CHO and 45 calories.

Note: This recipe is *not* suitable for freezing.

Oaty Top Blackberry & Apple

Serves 6 Total CHO – 150g Total Cals – 890

1 medium cooking apple, sliced
1×10oz (275g) can blackberries in natural juice
3oz (75g) oats
3oz (75g) unsweetened muesli
1 tablespoon vegetable oil
Liquid sweetener or Diamin *to taste*

1. Place apple and blackberries (with juice) in a casserole dish.
2. Mix remaining ingredients. Sprinkle over fruit.
3. Microwave on HIGH for 6 minutes. Allow to stand for 5 minutes.

Each portion is 25g CHO and 150 calories.

Note: This recipe is *not* suitable for freezing.

Baked Stuffed Apple

Serves 1 Total CHO – 20g Total Cals – 85

1 medium cooking apple
½oz (15g) currants
1 tablespoon water

1. Remove core from apple.
2. Fill with fruit.
3. Place stuffed apple and water in a dish. Cover with cling film – pierce the top.
4. Microwave on HIGH for 3-4 minutes.

Note: This recipe is *not* suitable for freezing.

Dried Fruit Compote

Serves 4 Total CHO – 100g Total Cals – 400

1 pint (550ml) boiling water
4oz (100g) dried whole apricots
2oz (50g) prunes
2oz (50g) dried dates
1 cinnamon stick or 1 teaspoon dried cinnamon

1. Place the boiling water in a 2 pint glass bowl. Stir in remaining ingredients. Cover with cling film and pierce the top.
2. Microwave on HIGH for 5 minutes. Stir, re-cover and microwave on HIGH for 6 minutes. Allow to stand for 20 minutes.
3. Chill before serving.

Each portion is 25g CHO and 100 calories.

Note: This recipe is *not* suitable for freezing.

Pouring Custard

Makes 1 pint Total CHO – 50g Total Cals – 270

1 pint (550ml) skimmed milk
2 tablespoons custard powder
Liquid sweetener to taste

1. Make a paste from 3 tablespoons of milk and the custard powder.
2. Microwave the remaining milk to boiling in a large jug.
3. Pour onto paste and stir well. Return custard to jug.
4. Microwave on HIGH for 2 minutes. Stir.
5. Microwave on HIGH for 1 minute. Serve.

Note: This recipe is *not* suitable for freezing.

Trifle

Serves 6 Total CHO – 95g Total Cals – 1330

Jelly
1×15oz (410g) can fruit cocktail in natural juice
½oz (15g/1 sachet) gelatine
A little low-sugar/ sugar-free squash to colour juice

Custard
2 tablespoons custard powder
½ pint (275ml) skimmed milk
Liquid sweetener to taste

Topping
½ pint (275ml) whipping cream

1. Drain fruit (reserving juice) and place in bottom of bowl.
2. Make juice up to ½ pint (275ml) with water.
3. Place 2 tablespoons water in a jug or glass and microwave on HIGH for 2 minutes. Stir in gelatine. Mix well.
4. Stir squash and gelatine into juice. Pour over fruit and leave to set.
5. Make a paste from 3 tablespoons milk and custard powder. Microwave remaining milk to boiling in a large jug.
6. Pour onto paste and stir well. Return to jug.
7. Microwave on HIGH for 2 minutes. Stir.
8. Microwave on HIGH for 1 minute. Pour over jelly and leave to cool.
9. Top with whipped cream and serve.

Each portion is 15g CHO and 220 calories.

Note: This recipe is *not* suitable for freezing.

Pineapple Bread Flan

Serves 8 Total CHO – 80g Total Cals – 820

4 medium slices wholemeal bread
1oz (25g) low-fat spread
Water to bind
4 pineapple rings (tinned in natural juice and drained) chopped
8oz (225g) cottage cheese
2×size 3 eggs

1. Liquidize bread on HIGH until fine breadcrumbs are achieved.
2. Mix in low-fat spread.
3. Add enough water to bring to a soft dough. Press into an 8in (20cm) glass flan ring.
4. Cook on HIGH for 4 minutes or until dry to the touch.
5. Mix remaining ingredients well. Pour into case.
6. Microwave on HIGH for 3 minutes – until just set.

Each portion is 10g CHO and 105 calories.

Note: This recipe is *not* suitable for freezing.

Special Chocolate Mousse

Serves 6 Total CHO – 60g Total Cals – 930

2 bars (150g) Special Recipe Chocolate
3 tablespoons skimmed milk
3×size 3 eggs, separated
½ oz (15g/1 sachet) gelatine

1. Place broken up chocolate and milk in a bowl. Microwave on MEDIUM until just melted.
2. Allow to cool slightly and beat in egg yolks.
3. Place 3 tablespoons of water in a glass. Microwave to boiling. Stir in gelatine and stir well. Beat in chocolate mixture.
4. Quickly beat egg white to stiff peaks and fold into chocolate.
5. Pour into 6 individual dishes and leave to set.

Each portion is 10g CHO and 155 calories.

Note: This recipe is *not* suitable for freezing.

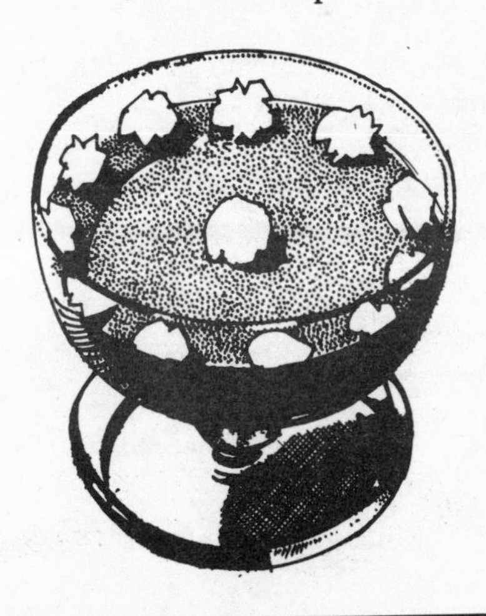

Blackberry Tarts

Makes 4 Total CHO – 65g Total Cals – 540

Crust
4 digestive biscuits, crushed
1oz (25g) low-fat spread, melted

Filling
8oz (225g) blackberries
2 tablespoons water
1 tablespoon fructose (fruit sugar)
1 tablespoon cornflour
¼ teaspoon cinnamon
1 tablespoon lemon juice

Meringue
1 egg white
1 teaspoon fructose (fruit sugar)
Pinch of cream of tartar
¼ teaspoon cinnamon

1. Mix the digestive biscuits and low-fat spread and press equally into 4 dishes. Microwave on HIGH for 1 minute.
2. Microwave blackberries, water and fructose on HIGH for 4-5 minutes.
3. Add other ingredients – blend cornflour with a little cold water beforehand.
4. Cook on HIGH for 2-3 minutes, stirring occasionally.
5. Pour over base.
6. Topping – whisk egg white until stiff, whisk in other ingredients.
7. Pile onto dishes.
8. Microwave on HIGH for about 1 minute.
9. Chill before serving.

Each tart is about 15g CHO and 135 calories.

Note: This recipe is *not* suitable for freezing.

Menu 5: Prawn Creole (page 23) and brown rice.

Menu 6: Kedgeree (page 25), green salad and Peaches with Loganberry Sauce (page 68).

Menu 7: Pork Casserole (page 45) and Special Chocolate Mousse (page 63).

Menu 8: Hummus (page 21) with pitta bread and Winter Veg Casserole (page 57).

Oaty Fruit

Serves 2 Total CHO – 50g Total Cals – 260

2oz (50g) rolled oats
½ pint (275ml) boiling water
1oz (25g) apricots, soaked and chopped
2 tablespoons natural low-fat yogurt

1. Soak oats in water for ¼ hour.
2. Mix in apricots.
3. Microwave on HIGH for 2 minutes. Stir well.
4. Microwave on HIGH for a further 2 minutes.
5. Allow to stand for 5 minutes. Stir in yogurt. Serve.

Each portion is 25g CHO and 130 calories.

Note: This recipe is *not* suitable for freezing.

Upside-down Pudding

Serves 6 Total CHO – 120g Total Cals – 1160

1×10oz (275g) can apricots, drained
3oz (75g) low-fat spread
1½oz (37g) fructose (fruit sugar)
2×size 3 eggs
5oz (150g) self-raising wholemeal flour
1 teaspoon baking powder
3 tablespoons skimmed milk

1. Place apricots in the base of a deep ceramic bowl.
2. Cream low-fat spread and fructose until light and creamy. Beat in eggs, fold in flour and baking powder. Add milk.
3. Pour over the fruit.
4. Microwave on HIGH for 6 minutes. Allow to stand for 5 minutes. Serve.

Each portion is 20g CHO and 195 calories.

Note: This recipe is *not* suitable for freezing.

Pears and Chocolate Sauce

Serves 4 Total CHO – 60g Total Cals – 320

4 eating pears, peeled and cored
½ pint (275ml) water

Chocolate Sauce
1 teaspoon cocoa
½ pint (275ml) skimmed milk
1 teaspoon wholemeal flour

1. Place pears and water in a large bowl. Microwave on HIGH for 4 minutes. Allow to cool.
2. Mix cocoa into milk. Microwave on HIGH for 1 minute.
3. Remove a little of the milk mixture, add to flour to make a smooth paste.
4. Return to rest of milk. Microwave on HIGH for 2 minutes. Stir.
5. Pour sauce over pears and serve.

Each portion, i.e. 1 pear plus sauce = 15g CHO and 80 calories.

Note: This recipe is *not* suitable for freezing.

Rice Pudding

Serves 3 Total CHO – 60g Total Cals – 285

2oz (50g) brown pudding rice
½oz (15g) currants
⅓ pint (180ml) skimmed milk

1. Place rice, currants and milk in a large bowl.
2. Microwave on HIGH for 4 minutes, stir.
3. Reduce heat to MEDIUM. Microwave for 15 minutes.
4. Allow to stand for 5 minutes.

Each portion is 20g CHO and 95 calories.

Note: This recipe is *not* suitable for freezing.

Pear and Ginger Pudding

Serves 5 Total CHO – 100g Total Cals – 1480

Topping

1oz (25g) low-fat spread, melted
1oz (25g) fructose (fruit sugar)
1×10oz (283g) can of pears in natural juice, drained

Pudding

4oz (100g) low-fat spread
2oz (50g) fructose (fruit sugar)
4oz (100g) wholemeal self-raising flour
2 teaspoons dried ginger
2×size 3 eggs
1 teaspoon baking powder
2 tablespoons water

1. Lightly oil a deep 1½ pint (825ml) oven proof dish. Place low-fat spread, fructose and pears in base of dish.
2. Beat all pudding ingredients together well until the mixture is smooth and glossy. Spread in the dish and cover with a piece of kitchen paper.
3. Microwave on HIGH for 6 minutes. Allow to stand for 5 minutes and turn out.

Each portion is 20g CHO and 300 calories.

Note: This recipe is *not* suitable for freezing.

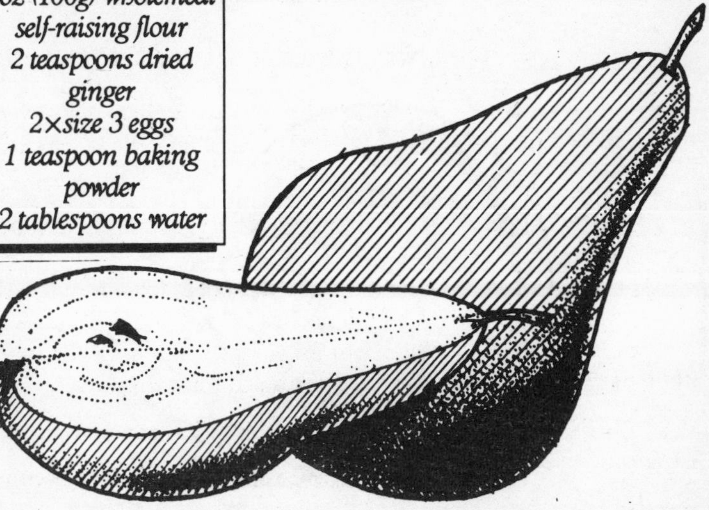

Peaches with Loganberry Sauce

Serves 4 Total CHO – 60g Total Cals – 260

4 peaches, slit around with a sharp knife
½ pint (275ml) water
A strip of orange rind

Sauce
1×10oz (275g) can loganberries in natural juice
Liquid sweetener to taste

1. Place peaches, water and rind in a large bowl. Cover with cling film and pierce the top.
2. Microwave on HIGH for 3 minutes. Turn peaches over, re-cover and microwave for a further 3 minutes.
3. Remove skin from peaches. Allow to cool.
4. Drain peaches.
5. Liquidize the loganberries in half of their juice. Sweeten to taste.
6. Spoon sauce over peaches to serve.

Each portion, i.e. 1 peach plus sauce = 15g CHO and 65 calories.

Note: This recipe is *not* suitable for freezing.

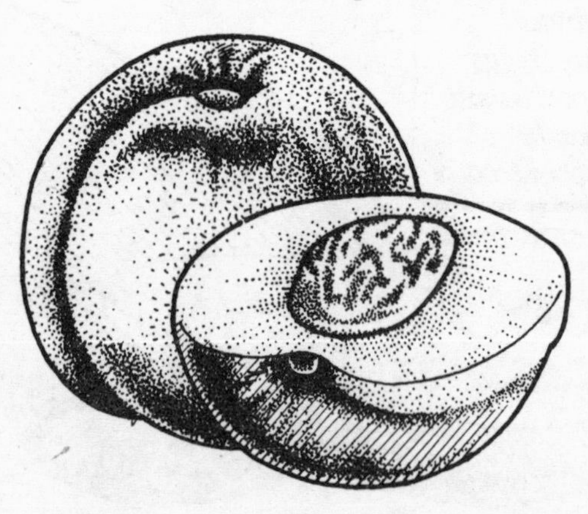

Apricot Loaf

Slices into 18 Total CHO – 90g Total Cals – 780

4oz (100g) wholemeal flour
2oz (50g) dried apricots, chopped
1 teaspoon mixed spice
1 teaspoon baking powder
1 teaspoon bicarbonate of soda
2oz (50g) low-fat spread
2×size 3 eggs
6 tablespoons skimmed milk
1 tablespoon lemon juice

1. Mix dry ingredients and low-fat spread, add the eggs. Mix the milk and lemon juice together and add to other ingredients, beat for 1 minute.
2. Pour into a lightly oiled 3 pint dish.
3. Microwave on MEDIUM for 2 minutes, turn, microwave for 2 minutes, turn and then microwave for a further minute.
4. Microwave on HIGH for 1 minute, turn, microwave for a further minute.
5. Allow to stand for 3 minutes.
6. Cool and slice.

Each slice is 5g CHO and 40 calories.

Note: This recipe freezes well.

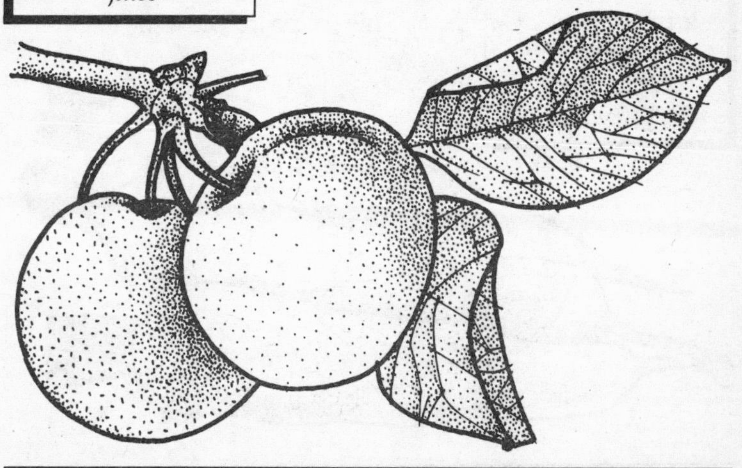

Carroty Muffins

Makes 12 Total CHO – 195g Total Cals – 1080

4oz (100g) bran flakes
3 fl oz (100ml) skimmed milk
4oz (100g) grated carrot
4oz (100g) self-raising 81% wholemeal flour
1 tablespoon fructose (fruit sugar)
2 tablespoons low-fat spread, melted
1 tablespoon lemon juice
1 teaspoon baking powder
½ teaspoon bicarbonate of soda
½ teaspoon cinnamon
¼ teaspoon salt
1×size 3 egg
2oz (50g) raisins

1. Mix bran flakes, milk and carrot. Soak for 10 minutes.
2. Add other ingredients.

Either

3. Half fill a lightly oiled tea cup with mixture. Microwave on HIGH for ½ to ¾ minute. Cool.
4. Repeat with rest of ingredients.

Or

Place the mixture in special muffin tins and microwave on HIGH for ½-¾ minute. Cool.

Each muffin is about 15g CHO and 90 calories.

Note: This recipe freezes well.

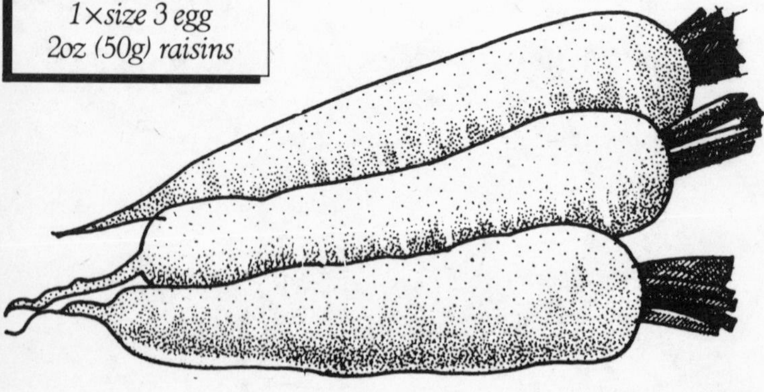

Orangy Raisin Muffins

Makes 10 Total CHO – 140g Total Cals – 920

2oz (50g) rolled oats
4oz (100g) wholemeal flour
2 tablespoons low-fat spread, melted
2 teaspoons baking powder
¼ teaspoon salt
2×size 3 eggs
2oz (50g) raisins
½ teaspoon grated orange rind
3 fl oz (100ml) skimmed milk

1. Mix all the ingredients together thoroughly.

Either

2. Lightly oil a small tea cup and half fill with mixture. Microwave on HIGH for ¼-½ a minute. Cool.
3. Repeat with remaining mixture.

Or

Place mixture in special muffin tins and microwave on HIGH for ¼-½ a minute. Cool.

Each muffin is 15g CHO and 90 calories.

Note: This recipe freezes well.

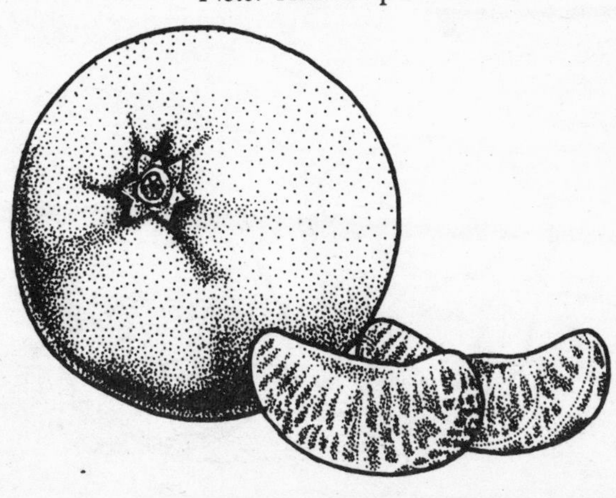

Vegetable Muffins

Makes 12 Total CHO – 125g Total Cals – 780

4oz (100g) 81% flour
2oz (50g) corn meal
1 tablespoon baking powder
Pinch of mixed herbs
Garlic salt to taste
2×size 3 eggs
1oz (25g) sweetcorn
1oz (25g) green pepper, chopped
1oz (25g) onion, finely chopped
1 tablespoon low-fat spread
1 teaspoon salt
4 tablespoons skimmed milk

1. Mix all the ingredients together.

Either

2. Lightly oil a small teacup and half fill with mixture. Microwave on HIGH for ¼-½ a minute. Cool.

3. Repeat with remaining mixture.

Or

Place mixture in special muffin tins and microwave on HIGH for ¼-½ a minute. Cool.

Each muffin is about 10g CHO and 65 calories.

Note: This recipe freezes well.

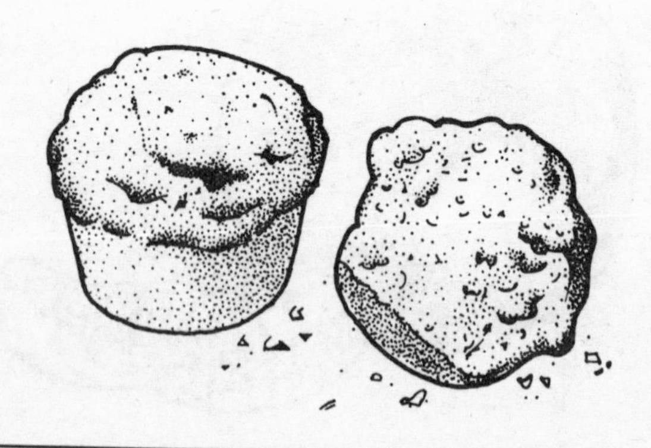

Cheesy Nut Scones

Makes 15 Total CHO – 150g Total Cals – 1230

2oz (50g) low-fat spread
8oz (225g) self-raising wholemeal flour
3oz (75g) reduced-fat hard cheese, grated
1 teaspoon dry mustard
1oz (25g) walnuts, chopped
A little skimmed milk

1. Rub low-fat spread into flour until it resembles fine breadcrumbs.
2. Add remaining dry ingredients and enough milk to bring to a dough.
3. Turn onto a floured board, knead for 5 minutes and roll to ½in (1cm) thick. Cut into 15 scones. Brush with a little milk.
4. Place on a pyrex or china plate and microwave on HIGH for 5 minutes.
5. Allow to stand for 5 minutes and serve immediately.

Each scone is 10g CHO and 80 calories.

Note: This mixture freezes well *uncooked* wrapped in foil.

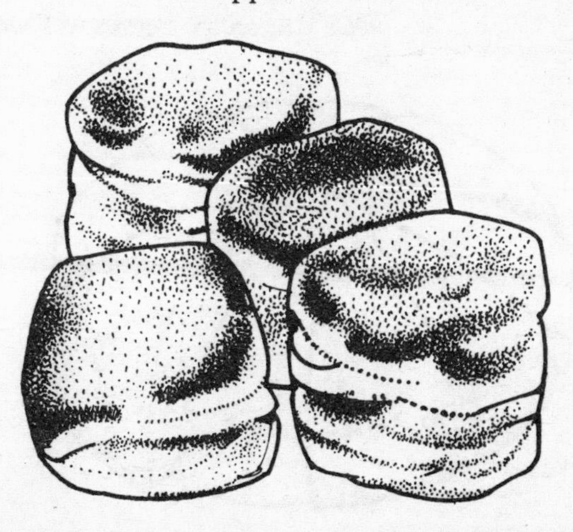

Soda Bread

Cuts into 10 large slices   Total CHO – 300g   Total Cals – 1580

1lb (450g) wholemeal flour
2 teaspoons bicarbonate of soda
2 teaspoons cream of tartar
1 teaspoon salt
1oz (25g) low-fat spread
¼ pint (150ml) skimmed milk
¼ pint (150ml) water

1. Mix flour, bicarbonate of soda, cream of tartar and salt. Rub in low-fat spread, mix milk and water together and add to the mixture. Mix to a dough.

2. Turn out onto a floured board and knead for 5 minutes. Form into a round. Mark into 10 with a knife. Cover a glass plate with greaseproof paper and place the dough on this.

3. Microwave on LOW for 7 minutes. Then on HIGH for 4-5 minutes. Allow to stand for 10 minutes.

Break into 10 – each portion is 30g CHO and 160 calories.

Note: This recipe freezes well wrapped in foil.

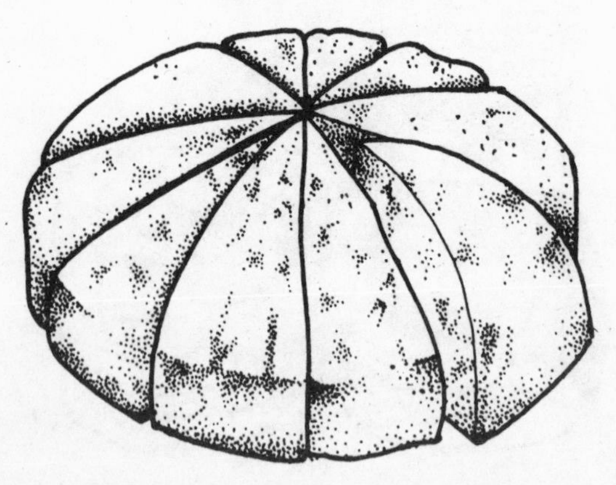

Fruit and Nut Scones

Makes 18 Total CHO – 180g Total Cals – 1130

2oz (50g) low-fat spread
8oz (225g) self-raising wholemeal flour
2oz (50g) sultanas
1oz (25g) hazelnuts, chopped
A little skimmed milk

1. Rub low-fat spread into flour until it resembles fine breadcrumbs. Mix well with enough milk to bring to a dough.
2. Turn onto a floured board. Knead for 5 minutes. Roll to ½in (1cm) thick. Cut into 18.
3. Place on a pyrex or china plate. Microwave on HIGH for 5 minutes. Allow to stand for 5 minutes.
4. Serve immediately.

Each scone is 10g CHO and 65 calories.

Note: This mixture freezes well *uncooked*.

Nutty Chocolate Slice

Makes 16 Total CHO – 95g Total Cals – 1300

3oz (75g) low-fat spread
1oz (25g) cocoa
2oz (50g) fructose (fruit sugar)
2×size 3 eggs, beaten
2 tablespoons skimmed milk
1 teaspoon vanilla essence
4oz (100g) 81% self-raising flour
2oz (50g) hazelnuts

1. Place low-fat spread and cocoa in a bowl. Melt on high for 2 minutes.
2. Add fructose, eggs, milk and essence. Stir in flour and nuts. Pour into a large rectangular dish.
3. Cover the corner of the dish with foil. (Check the instructions of your machine about the foil.)
4. Microwave on HIGH for 5 minutes. Allow to stand for 10 minutes. Cool in the dish. Slice into 16.

Each slice is 5g CHO and 80 calories.

Note: This recipe is *not* suitable for freezing.

Easy Fruit Cake

Slices into 22 Total CHO – 655g Total Cals – 3760

¼ pint (150ml) sunflower oil
7oz (200g) raisins
7oz (200g) currants
7oz (200g) sultanas
5oz (150g) dates, chopped
¼ pint (150ml) skimmed milk
9oz (250g) wholemeal flour
1 teaspoon mixed spice
2×size 3 eggs
½ teaspoon bicarbonate of soda

1. Beat all ingredients together well.
2. Pour into a large dish, or ceramic cake tin. Cover with cling film and pierce the top.
3. Microwave on MEDIUM for 30 minutes. Allow to stand in a dish for 30 minutes. Slice into 22.

Each slice is 30g CHO and 170 calories.

Note: This recipe freezes well.

Mixed Grain Bread

Makes 16 slices Total CHO – 310g Total Cals – 1440

9oz (250g) 81% flour
2oz (50g) rye flour
2oz (50g) rolled oats
1oz (25g) corn meal
1 packet (14g) easy blend yeast
3 tablespoons black treacle
1 tablespoon low-fat spread, melted
1 teaspoon salt
7 fl oz (200ml) water
Wheatgerm/ poppy seeds/ sesame seeds, etc.

1. Mix the flours and yeast together. Add treacle, low-fat spread, salt and water.
2. Add remaining wholewheat flour to give a soft pliable dough.
3. Knead well. Leave to rise in a greased, loosely sealed poly bag until it doubles in size.
4. Knock down and shape into a sausage, then into an 8in (20cm) ring.
5. Brush with water and coat with seeds.
6. Leave covered until again it doubles in size.
7. Microwave on MEDIUM for 6 minutes, then on HIGH for 3 minutes. Leave to cool.

Each slice is 20g CHO and 90 calories.

Note: This recipe freezes well.

6. *Preserving*

Use your microwave to make speedy preserves

See notes on pages 15-16 before you begin!

Strawberry Jam

Yield 1lb 6oz (625g) Total CHO – 215g* *or* 40g**
Total Cals – 865

1lb (450g) strawberries
1 large cooking apple
½ pint (275ml) water
6oz (175g) fructose (fruit sugar)

1. Place fruit with water in a glass bowl. Microwave on HIGH for 10 minutes.
2. Add fructose, stir and microwave for 7 minutes.
3. Stir, microwave for 25 minutes, stirring every 5 minutes.

CHO – 2g per ounce (if fructose is *not* included in the calculation)
– 10g per ounce (if fructose *is* included in the calculation)
Cals – 40 per ounce

* If fructose *is* included
** If fructose is *not* included

Lemon Curd

Yield 12oz (350g) Total CHO – 230g* *or* 5g**
Total Cals – 1435

3oz (75g) low-fat spread
2 lemons, rind and juice
8oz (225g) fructose (fruit sugar)
3 eggs

1. Place low-fat spread in a large glass bowl – microwave on HIGH for 30 seconds.
2. Add remaining ingredients – microwave on HIGH for 3 minutes.
3. Stir mixture at the end of each minute.
4. Microwave for 1½ minutes, stirring briskly each ½ minute.
5. Microwave for another 4 minutes, stirring after each minute.

CHO – negligible per ounce (if fructose is *not* included in the calculation)
– 19g per ounce (if fructose *is* included in the calculation)
Cals – 120 per ounce

* If fructose *is* included
** If fructose is *not* included

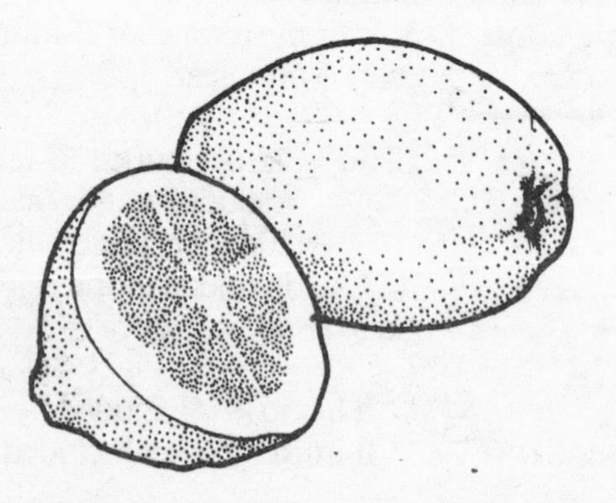

Apple Chutney

Yield 3lb (1¼kg) Total CHO – 135g Total Cals – 530

2lb (900g) cooking apples, peeled, cored and sliced
Pinch of garlic salt
1 pint (550ml) vinegar
4oz (100g) sultanas
¼ teaspoon salt
1 teaspoon ground ginger
Cayenne pepper
Mixed spice

1. Place the apples in a bowl with the garlic and half the vinegar. Cover with cling film and pierce the top.
2. Microwave on HIGH for 6 minutes. Stir.
3. Add remaining vinegar and ingredients. Replace cling film.
4. Microwave on HIGH for 5 minutes, stir and re-cover.
5. Microwave on HIGH for 10 minutes. Stir after each 5 minutes.

CHO – 3g per ounce
Cals – 10 per ounce

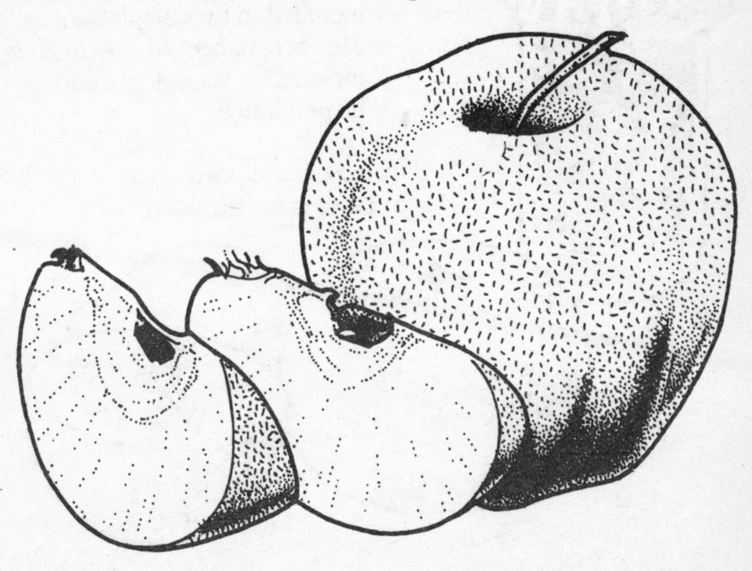

Lemon and Grapefruit Marmalade

Yield 1lb 7oz (650g) Total CHO – 490g* *or* 40g**
Total Cals – 1960

1½lb (675g) grapefruit
1 large lemon
1lb (450g) fructose (fruit sugar)
1½ pints (825ml) water

1. Place juice, flesh, peel and 8oz (225g) of fructose in a bowl.
2. Microwave on HIGH for 8 minutes.
3. Add ¾ pint of water. Microwave on HIGH for 5 minutes.
4. Add remaining fructose. Microwave on HIGH for 5 minutes.
5. Add remaining water and microwave on HIGH for 50-60 minutes, stirring every 10 minutes.

CHO – 2g per ounce (if fructose is *not* included in the calculation)
– 21g per ounce (if fructose *is* included in the calculation)
Cals – 85 per ounce

* If fructose *is* included
** If fructose is *not* included

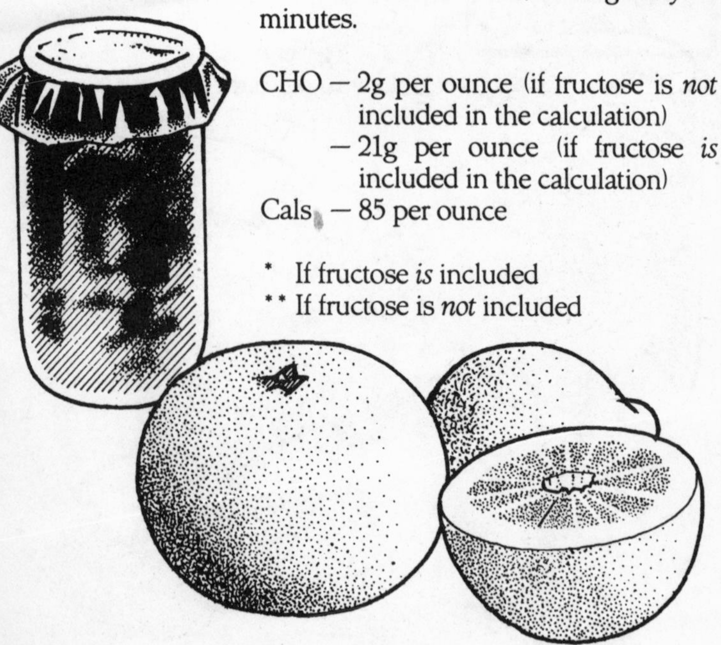

3 Fruit Marmalade

Yield 2lb (900g) Total CHO – 710g* *or* 35g**
Total Cals – 2855

¾lb (350g) grapefruit
1 large lemon
6oz (175g) sweet oranges
1½lb (675g) fructose (fruit sugar)
1½ pints (825ml) water

1. Place juice, flesh and peel of all the fruit and 8oz (225g) of fructose in a bowl. Microwave on HIGH for 8 minutes.
2. Add ¾ pint water – microwave on HIGH for 5 minutes.
3. Add remaining fructose – microwave on HIGH for 5 minutes.
4. Add remaining water – microwave on HIGH for 50-60 minutes, stirring every 10 minutes.

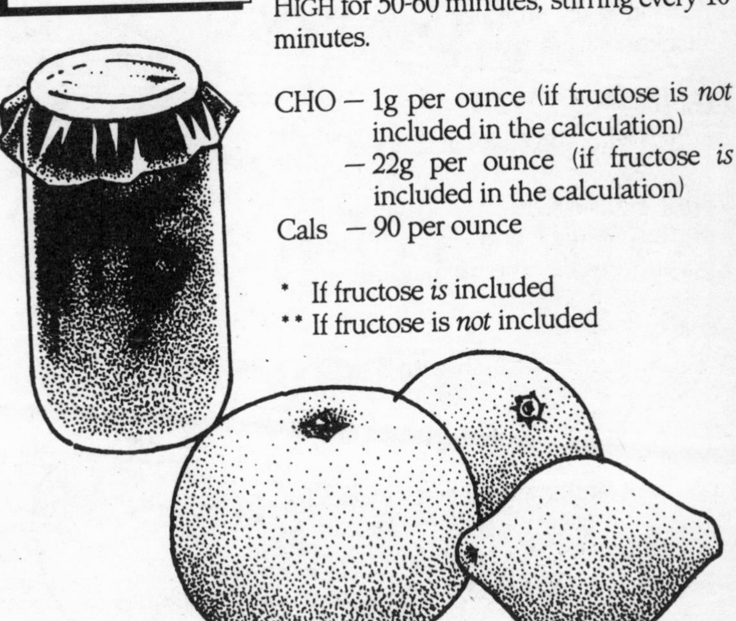

CHO – 1g per ounce (if fructose is *not* included in the calculation)
– 22g per ounce (if fructose *is* included in the calculation)

Cals – 90 per ounce

* If fructose *is* included
** If fructose is *not* included

7. Menu Suggestions

Some menu suggestions for you to fit into your allowances

MENU 1

A lunch with 30g CHO and under 300 calories

	CHO	*Cals*
1 slice Tuna Bread Flan (page 24)	10g	120
1 portion Spicy Summer Veg (see page 57)	5g	30
1 Blackberry Tart (page 64)	15g	135

MENU 2

A lunch with 40g CHO and under 450 calories

1 portion Liver Casserole (page 44)	10g	240
1 portion Spinach and Cheese Bake (page 56)	5g	105
1 portion Fruit Compote (page 60)	25g	100

MENU 3

A warming winter lunch with 50g CHO and under 350 calories

1 portion Spicy Red Soup (page 18)	10g	50
1 piece Soda Bread (page 74)	30g	160
1 portion Cauliflower Cheese (page 35)	10g	110

MENU 4

A bedtime snack with 20g CHO and under 150 calories

1 Cheesy Nut Scone (page 73)	10g	80
1 medium orange	10g	40

	CHO	*Cals*

MENU 5
An evening meal with 50g CHO and under 300 calories

1 Fruit Kebab (page 22)	10g	40
1 portion Prawn Creole (page 23)	5g	65
1 portion Brown Rice (1½oz dry weight)	30g	120
1 portion Lime Soufflé (page 58)	5g	45

MENU 6
An evening meal with 60g CHO and under 500 calories

1 portion Kedgeree (page 25)	45g	390
1 portion Green Salad	*neg*	10
1 Peach with Loganberry Sauce (page 68)	15g	65

MENU 7
A celebration meal with 50g CHO and under 600 calories

1 portion Pork Casserole (page 45)	10g	295
1 Jacket Potato (5oz raw)	30g	130
1 portion Special Chocolate Mousse (page 63)	10g	155

MENU 8
A Vegetarian meal with 70g and under 550 calories

1 small portion Hummus (page 21)	5g	60
Half a wholemeal pitta bread	20g	90
1 portion Winter Vegetable Casserole (page 57)	5g	30
1 portion Wholewheat Spaghetti Flan (page 32)	20g	150
1 portion Upside-down Pudding (page 65)	20g	195

Appendix: Food Values List

Food	*Amount*	gCHO	*Cals*
Apple — cooking, whole	1 lb (450g)	35	140
— eating, whole	1	10	40
Apricots — canned in natural juice	1×14oz (410g) can	40	190
— dried, stoned	1oz (25g)	12	50
Aubergines — as bought	1lb (450g)	11	50
Bacon — lean	1lb (450g)	—	675
Banana — peeled	1 medium	10	40
Beans — Aduki (soaked & cooked)	1oz (25g)	5	25
— Red Kidney (canned)	1×15oz (425g) can	64	330
— Frozen Green	1oz (25g)	1	5
— Butter (canned)	1×15oz (425g) can	50	280
Beansprouts	1lb (450g)	10	50
Beef stock	1 cube	*neg*	*neg*
Blackberries — fresh/frozen	4oz (100g)	7	30
Black treacle	1oz (25g)	17	65
Bran flakes	1oz(25g)	19	90
Bread — wholemeal	1oz (25g)	12	60
Broccoli — as bought	1lb (450g)	10	90
Brown Ale	1×275ml can	11	110
Carrot — raw as bought	1lb (450g)	20	90
Cashew nuts	1oz (25g)	7	140
Cauliflower — raw as bought	1lb (450g)	6	50

Food	*Amount*	*gCHO*	*Cals*
Celery — fresh raw	1lb (450g)	5	30
Cheese — reduced-fat, hard	1oz (25g)	—	80
Chick peas — canned	1×15oz (425g) can	60	280
Chicken — lean white meat	1lb (450g)	—	540
Chicken breasts — skinned	1lb (450g)	—	490
Chicken stock — cube	1 cube	*neg*	*neg*
Chocolate — Special Recipe	1oz (25g)	10	115
Cocoa	1oz (25g)	10	110
Cod fillets	1lb (450g)	—	300
Cornflour	1oz (25g)	25	90
Cornmeal	1oz (25g)	18	95
Cottage cheese	1oz (25g)	*neg*	27
Courgettes — raw, whole	1lb (450g)	15	100
Cream — whipping	1oz (25g)	½	80
Custard Powder	1oz (25g)	25	90
Currants — dried	1oz (25g)	18	70
Dates	1oz (25g)	18	70
Digestive biscuits	1	10	70
Eggs — raw	1×size 3	—	75
Fish stock	1 cube	*neg*	*neg*
Flour — wholemeal, plain/S.R.	1oz (25g)	18	90
Flour — 81%, plain/S.R.	1oz (25g)	19	92
Fructose (fruit sugar)	1oz (25g)	30*	115
Fruit cocktail in natural juice	1×14oz (410g) can	50	190
Gelatine	1 sachet	—	35
Grapefruit — fresh whole	1 large	10	45
Green pepper	1lb (450g)	10	70
Haddock — smoked	1lb (450g)	—	330
Hazelnuts — shelled	1oz (25g)	2	110
Leeks — raw, as bought	1lb (450g)	30	140
Lemon — raw	1	*neg*	10

**Note:* Usually ignored if less than 1oz (25g) taken in a day.

Food	*Amount*	*gCHO*	*Cals*
Lentils, red, green and orange	1oz (25g)	15	85
Liver — lamb's, raw	1lb (450g)	7	800
Loganberries in natural juice	1×10oz (284g) can	20	90
Low-fat spread	1oz (25g)	—	105
Mackerel in brine	1×5oz (150g) can	—	175
Milk — skimmed, fresh	1 pint	30	190
Minced beef — very lean	1lb (450g)	—	820
Mushrooms — whole raw	1lb (450g)	—	70
Mushroom soup	1×10oz (284g) can	40	370
Oatmeal/oats raw	1oz (25g)	20	110
Oil	1 fl oz	—	255
Onion — raw as bought	1lb (450g)	25	100
Orange	1 medium	10	40
Parsnips — raw as bought	1lb (450g)	40	160
Pasta — wholegrain, raw, dry	1oz (25g)	19	95
Peaches — fresh, whole	1 large	10	40
— in natural juice	1×14oz (410g) can	45	180
Pears — fresh, whole	1 large	10	40
Peas — green, frozen	4oz (100g)	7	55
Pineapple — in natural juice	1×15oz (425g) can	55	240
Pineapple juice	¼ pint (150ml)	18	70
Pork — shoulder, lean, raw	1lb (450g)	—	830
Potato — raw as bought	1lb (450g)	80	340
Prawns — peeled, raw	4oz (100g)	—	110
Prunes — stoned, dried, whole	1oz (25g)	10	40
Raisins, dried	1oz (25g)	18	70
Red pepper, raw as bought	1lb (450g)	10	70
Rice — brown long grain, raw	1oz (25g)	20	95
Rye flour	1oz (25g)	20	85
Soya sauce		*neg*	*neg*

Food	*Amount*	*gCHO*	*Cals*
Spinach — boiled & drained	1lb (450g)	6	140
Squash — low sugar/low calorie	¼ pint (150ml)	—	<5
Stewing Steak — lean	1lb (450g)	—	790
Strawberries — fresh	1lb (450g)	27	110
Sweetcorn — tinned, kernels	1×11oz (310g) can	55	250
Tomato — juice	¼ pint (150ml)	6	30
— purée	1oz (25g)	4	20
Tomatoes — canned	1×14oz (410g) can	10	50
Tuna in brine	1×7oz (120g) can	—	220
Vinegar	¼ pint (150ml)	—	5
Walnuts — shelled	1oz (25g)	1½	150
White Wine — dry	4 fl oz (100ml)	1	80
Yogurt — low-fat natural	1×5oz (150g) carton	10	80

Recommended Reading

These books contain lots of helpful information and many recipes which you can use in your packed lunches and snacks.

Countdown
(Published by The British Diabetic Association)
A guide to carbohydrate and calorie content of manufactured foods.

Better Cookery for Diabetics
(Published by The British Diabetic Association)
A recipe book by Jill Metcalfe.

Cooking the New Diabetic Way
(Published by The British Diabetic Association)
A recipe book by Jill Metcalfe.

Simple Diabetic Cookery
(Published by The British Diabetic Association)
A recipe leaflet.

The Vegetarian on a Diet
(Published by Thorsons Publishing Group, 1984)
A recipe book for vegetarians by Margaret Cousins and Jill Metcalfe.

Christmas Cookery
(Published by The British Diabetic Association)
A leaflet with a range of traditional Christmas recipes.

Home Preserving
(Published by The British Diabetic Association)
A leaflet with a range of jam, marmalade and chutney recipes.

Cooking for Diabetes
(Published by Thorsons Publishing Group, 1985)
A recipe book by Jill Metcalfe.

Packed Lunches and Snacks
(Published by Thorsons Publishing Group, 1986)
A recipe book by Sue Hall.

Note: None of the above are microwave books but they are all *very* suitable for diabetics. The recipes can be adapted to any microwave (using the instruction book for your oven).

Further Information

BRITISH DIABETIC ASSOCIATION

Diabetes affects just over two per cent of the population of the UK. Although it cannot be cured or prevented, it can be controlled by proper treatment.

The *British Diabetic Association* (BDA) was formed in 1934 to help all diabetics, to overcome prejudice and ignorance about diabetes, and to raise money for research towards a cure. The Association is currently budgeting £1.5m each year to this end, and is the largest single contributor to diabetic research in the UK.

The Association is an independent organization with over 100,000 members and 350 local branches. It provides a welfare and advisory service for diabetics and their families. It also liaises closely with those who work in the field of diabetes.

Educational and activity holidays are organized for diabetics of all ages plus parent/child and parent/teenager weekends.

Members receive the BDA's bi-monthly magazine *Balance* which keeps readers up to date with news of the latest research and all aspects of diabetes.

All diabetics have to follow a lifelong diet and *Balance* publishes recipes and dietary information to help bring interest and variety in eating.

To become a member, fill in the application form and send it with your subscription to:

British Diabetic Association,
10 Queen Anne Street,
London W1M 0BD.
Tel: 01-323 1531

Enrolment Form

British Diabetic Association
10 Queen Anne Street
London W1M 0BD

MEMBERSHIP SUBSCRIPTIONS

Life membership	Single payment of £105 or £15 a year for 7 years under covenant
Annual membership	£5.00 a year
Reduced membership – pensioner, student on Government grant and those in receipt of DHSS benefits.	£1.00 a year
Overseas annual membership	£10.00 a year
Overseas life membership	Single payment of £150.00

Please enrol me as a:

- ☐ Life member: £105
  £15 a year for 7 years under covenant
- ☐ Annual member: £5.00
- ☐ Pensioner member: £1.00
- ☐ Overseas annual member: £10.00
- ☐ Overseas Life member: £150.00
- ☐ Are you joining on behalf of a child? (Children in the UK under the age of 16 can join free for one year if they wish)

I enclose Remittance/Banker's Order/Covenant for £ ....
(Please delete whichever does not apply)

Date .... Signature ....

Full name: Mr/Mrs/Miss ....
(Block Capitals please)

Address ....

....

Date of Birth .... Occupation ....
(This information will be treated as strictly confidential)

COVENANT

I/we, ...(full name), of

....(address)

covenant with the British Diabetic Association that for four ☐ or seven years ☐ from the present date or during my lifetime (whichever period shall the shorter) I/we will pay to the Association on the

....(this date

should be the same as, or later than, the date of the signature) in every year such a sum as, after deduction of income tax for the time being in force, amounts to £ ....

(insert actual amount you wish to pay).

(Indicate by tick in box).

Signed, sealed and delivered by me/us this .... day of .... 19 ......

Signature ....

Signature of witness ....

Address of witness ....

BANKER'S ORDER

To .... Bank .... Branch,

....(address)

Date .... Please pay to the National Westminster Bank Ltd, 154 Harley Street, London W1 (60 10 02) now and on .... (date) each year for four years ☐, seven years ☐ or until further notice ☐ the sum of .... pounds for the credit of the British Diabetic Association (A/c No. 12773085)

(Indicate by tick in box)

Signed ....

Name ....

(Block Capitals Please)

Address ....

.... A/c No. ....

Please return the completed Covenant/Banker's Order to:

BRITISH DIABETIC ASSOCIATION

10 Queen Anne Street, London W1M 0BD. Tel: 01-323 1531.

Index